A History of
THE FULLER'S E
MINING INDUS
AROUND BATH

Neil Macmillen

with Mike Chapman

'You are probably aware that fuller's earth is a valuable product, and that it is only found in one or two places in England.'
A. Conan Doyle, 'The Adventure of the Engineer's Thumb',
The Adventures of Sherlock Holmes, 1891-1892

'Not the whole art of man can make a pot of it.' Anon

 Lightmoor Press

General Map of the area south of Bath showing the fuller's earth sites with grid references

KEY

1. *Evergreen Fuller's EarthWorks, Rush Hill (ST734626)*
2. *Wansdyke Fuller's Earth Works (ST738618)*
3. *Top Works and adits, Horsecombe Vale (ST753617)*
4. *The Pan Works, Horsecome Vale) (ST754061850*
5. *Tucking Mill Fuller's Earth Works (ST76556160)*
6. *Hodshill Mines (ST74656075)*
7. *South Stoke Fuller's Earth Works at Underhill (ST74636045)*
8. *The Hayes Mines, Wellow (ST732585)*
9. *Wellow Fuller's Earth Works (ST74005820)*
10. *Hassage Hill Mines, Wellow (ST742576)*
11. *Combe Hay Lower Works (ST73356120)*
12. *Combe Hay Upper Works, Odd Down (ST72956115)*
13. *The 'Duchy' open-cast Mines (ST729618)*
14. *Vernham Wood Mine (ST73206175)*
15. *The 'Grove' Mine, Combe Hay (ST73556120)*

MIKE CHAPMAN

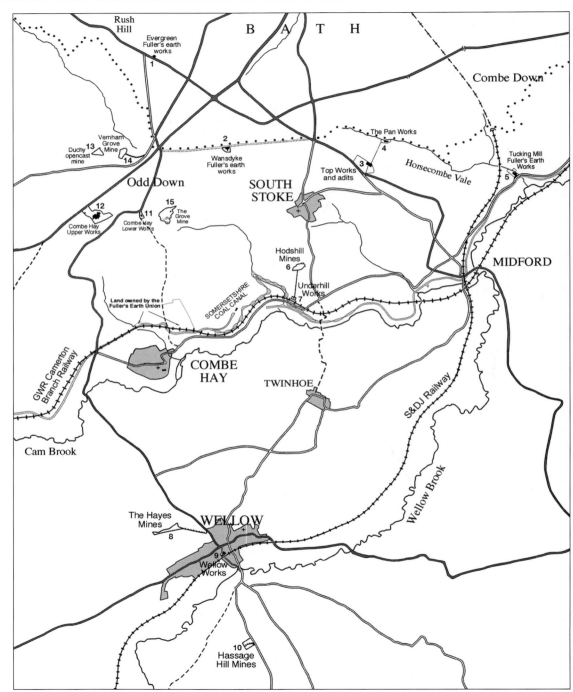

CONTENTS

Published by LIGHTMOOR PRESS
© Lightmoor Press, Neil Macmillen & Mike Chapman 2009
Designed by Neil Parkhouse

British Library Cataloguing-in-Publication Data. A catalogue
record for this book is available from the British Library

ISBN 13: 9781899889 32 7

LIGHTMOOR PRESS
Unit 144B, Lydney Trading Estate, Harbour Road, Lydney, Gloucestershire GL15 5EJ
www.lightmoor.co.uk
Lightmoor Press is an imprint of Black Dwarf Lightmoor Publications Ltd

Printed & bound by Information Press, Eynsham, Oxford

BLOWING IN THE WIND
An Introduction

For over eight years, the former Fuller's Earth Works on Odd Down had lain derelict when, in 1988, a local man, walking his dog near the works, noticed pieces of paper blowing in the wind. On closer inspection, they proved to be documents of the Fullers' Earth Union, which children had found in the loft above the former office. They had been making fires from some of the papers. Fortunately, he notified the Museum of Bath at Work and in the following days, some 100,000 documents consisting of letters, time cards and plans were recovered and sorted.

During the next few years, the Museum worked to classify the papers and to produce a synopsis of the correspondence of the company. The Museum has retained these records as Laporte Industries Ltd, at that time the owners of the site, expressed no further interest in them. It is from these papers that much information about the industry has been obtained.

This book would not have been possible without the information and photographs that have been contributed by a large number of people. In particular, I should like to thank the staff at Avon Industrial Buildings Trust, who enabled me to start the project, and to Stuart Burroughs, Director of the Museum of Bath at Work, who through the years has overseen the classification of the records. Alison Smith did a tremendous job in producing the synopsis of the correspondence dating from 1915 to 1951, whilst Mike Chapman has constantly encouraged me to complete the project and has been responsible for all the graphical work. I am very grateful to Owen Ward for reading through the manuscript and for his helpful suggestions. Finally, I would like to thank most sincerely Bert Upshall of Odd Down, who was foreman at the works and without whose information and guidance this book would not have been possible.

Some confusion has arisen over the location of the works. This is because in the early correspondence of the Fullers' Earth Union they were addressed as the 'Combe Hay Works, Midford, Bath'. The inclusion of Midford may date from the time when there was an office at Tucking Mill in Midford. During the period that Laporte Industries Ltd owned and operated the site, it was known as 'Bath Fullers Earth Works, Odd Down', although in fact the site is within the parish of Combe Hay. The works were sited on two areas of the plateau south of Bath known as Folly and Pickett Downs.

Neil Macmillen, Bath, 2008

DEDICATION

This book is dedicated to Bert Upshall and all his former colleagues in the fuller's earth industry in Bath, in gratitude for all the help given over so many years to this project.

⊰ Chapter 1 ⊱

'THIS USEFUL EARTH'

The Early History of Fuller's Earth in the Bath area

In the words of the Rev'd Richard Warner, writing in 1811, the deposits of fuller's earth around Bath were still '… *applicable to all the purposes to which this useful earth is usually applied.*' For centuries, until the coming of modern soaps and detergents, this particular form of clay was commonly used for absorbing the grease and dirt from natural wool or soiled cloth, by mixing it into a thin cream with water. The Romans would have discovered these deposits on the south side of Bath whilst building the Fosse Way across Folly Down and may have exploited the seams on Odd Down where, it has been suggested, there was a scattering of various Roman settlements for nearly four centuries. The probable method of extraction was by digging 'bell-pits' up to some 40 feet in depth but the cost of transporting the heavy clay may be the reason why several of the Roman villas in the area were located close to readily available deposits. Near a villa in the parish of Combe Hay, for instance, several 2nd century burials and a complete Romano-British settlement were discovered adjacent to the last fuller's earth mine in 1967, together with evidence of a wide variety of small scale industrial activities. Again, in the neighbouring parishes of Southstoke, on Hodshill, and Wellow, in Upper Hayes, Roman remains have been located near fuller's earth workings.

Almost certainly these villas would have had a *fullonica*, where fabrics were cleaned or 'fulled' in a mixture of the earth and water. The *fullonica* was an important part of the Roman household, because it was here that the *fullo*, the laundry or bath man, was responsible for cleaning the garments of the house. The Romans knew this clay-like substance as *creta fullonia*, literally 'fuller's clay', and the clods of earth would have been brought to the house in barrels or open carts from shallow pits or nearby outcrops. The fulling process (as illustrated on reliefs at Pompeii) was carried out in wooden troughs some 0.75m (2.5ft) long and 0.6m (2ft) wide. An example of such a trough was discovered on the site of the 3rd century Roman barn at Littlecote Manor, near Hungerford, on the Wiltshire-Berkshire border. This had evidently been used for cleaning fleeces from the flocks kept on the nearby hills and suggests that fuller's earth from the Bath area was being used to treat Cotswold wool during the Roman occupation.

The most important use of fulling, however, was in the finishing of newly woven cloth, which was first soaked in stale urine or other alkaline solution and then trampled in a trough or vat containing a slurry of fuller's earth. In medieval times, this process was originally called 'waulking', because the fullers literally walked on the cloth. To remove the earth after it absorbed the oil in the fibres, the cloth was first rinsed with clean water and then 'tentered', *i.e.* stretched into shape (from 'tenter-hooks') on racks, to dry in the open air. Such rough treatment

Romano-British remains at the Combe Hay fuller's earth mine. View of stone coffin, entrance sill and wall foundations, showing the mill stone and bits of pottery. These were discovered when a new entrance to the mine was opened in 1967.
LAPORTE NEWS, VOL. 8, NO. 5, DECEMBER 1969

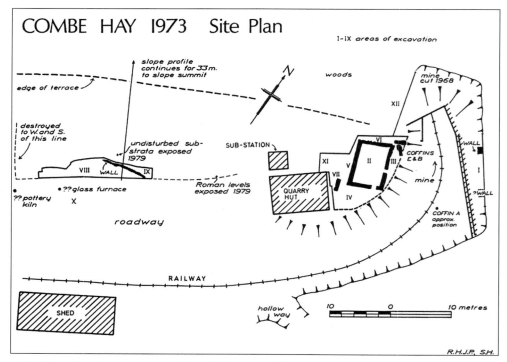

COMBE HAY 1973   Site Plan

I-IX *areas of excavation*

slope profile
continues for 33m.
to slope summit

edge of terrace

woods

mine
cut 1968

XII

destroyed
to W. and S.
of this line

undisturbed sub-
strata exposed
1979

SUB-STATION

WALL

VI

COFFINS
E & B

Roman levels
exposed 1979

VIII   WALL   IX

XI   V   II   III

I

mine

?WALL

??glass furnace

QUARRY
HUT

VII

??pottery
kiln   X

IV

COFFIN A
approx.
position

roadway

RAILWAY

SHED

hollow
way

10   0   *10 metres*

R.H.J.P. S.H.

Site Plan of area known as
the Grove Mine showing
where Roman remains were
found in 1967.
BASED ON THE PROCEEDINGS
OF THE SOMERSET
ARCHAEOLOGY & NATURAL
HISTORY SOCIETY, 1980,
WITH ADDITIONS

gave rise to another term for this process – 'tucking' – derived from a word signifying a physical beating or punishment. Moreover, if the scouring was sufficiently vigorous, considerable heat could be generated, causing the fabric to shrink and the fibres to felt. The result was a thicker and denser cloth, which not only made garments windproof and less permeable but also more comfortable to wear.

This method of thickening the cloth (later known as 'milling') was most effectively achieved by the use of a machine called a fulling stock, which could maintain a violent pounding action for many hours. This device, which first appeared in this country at the end of the 11th century, was usually powered by a water-wheel and consisted of two large, heavy wooden hammers or mallets (the 'stocks') hinged side by side, which were alternately lifted and dropped by revolving cams in a treading action into the fulling trough below. The heavily felted cloth produced by this method, the much sought after 'broadcloth', may well have been the reason for the rise to national prominence of the woollen industry in this part of the West Country from the 13th century onwards. It was here that all the best conditions existed for its production – the abundant water-power to drive the stocks from the swiftly flowing streams of the Cotswolds and broken hill country of the Avon Valley, and the supply of fine short wool from the flocks grazing on the surrounding downlands. The other essential requirement was the readily available fuller's earth from local pits which, over the centuries, must have produced vast quantities of the material for these processes.

At a national level, the value and importance of fuller's earth later became such that, in the words of Thomas Pennant, in his *Journal from Chester to London*, 1811, '… *the British legislature therefore, have from the days of Charles I, guarded against the exportation of it* [fuller's earth] *under severe penalties.*' The embargoes were enforced again by an Act of 1688 and repeated in 1693 and 1720, although this did not prevent it being smuggled out of the country. There was some relaxation, when an Act of Parliament dated 25th April 1807 permitted the export of fuller's earth and tobacco pipe clay to any place '*in the possession of His Majesty*' but exports to foreign countries were still prohibited. It was not until 1823 that this Act was finally repealed and the American market opened up to English fuller's earth. Exports across the Atlantic Ocean continued until they were interrupted by the American Civil War (1861-65).

Despite the constant demand for fuller's earth throughout the Middle Ages, little is known about the early workings near Bath. The city itself was well known as a prosperous cloth town during the 14th and 15th centuries and no doubt depended on the deposits of fuller's earth in the neighbourhood.

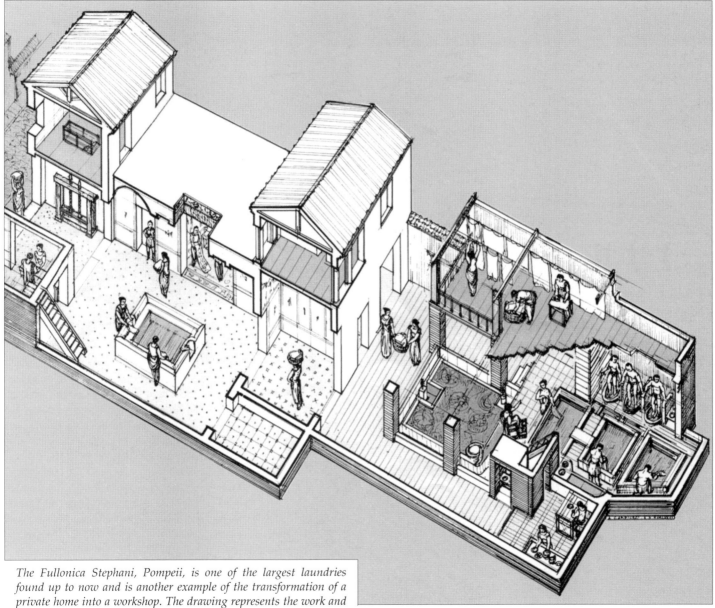

The Fullonica Stephani, Pompeii, is one of the largest laundries found up to now and is another example of the transformation of a private home into a workshop. The drawing represents the work and commercial cycle as it was in the Fullonica Stephani in the first half of the 1st century A.D. Dirty clothes arrived at the back of the fullonica, except for the more delicate clothes which were washed in the former atrium (centre left), using the impluvium, transformed into a tub equipped for this purpose (see photograph over page). Clothes with more resistant stains were literally trampled by workers in the three oval tubs (saltus fullonici); then, together with the other clothes, they were placed in larger tubs (see extreme right) and were gradually and carefully cleaned.

FROM POMPEII – TWO THOUSAND YEARS AGO AND TODAY, *PUBLISHED 1997 BY BONECHI EDIZIONE 'IL TURISMO'*

BELOW: Fulling Stocks.
a. *Cog wheel driven by a water wheel or steam engine.*
b. *Floor of the mill*
c. *Main driving shaft below the floor.*
d. *Cams, lifters or tappets on the driving shaft.*
e. *Curved beaters or hammer heads raised by the cams.*
f. *Stems of shafts of the hammers*
g. *Hammer pivots*
h. *Trough containing a mixture of fuller's earth and water.*
i. *Curved wooden breast of the trough.*
j. *Cloth being fulled.*

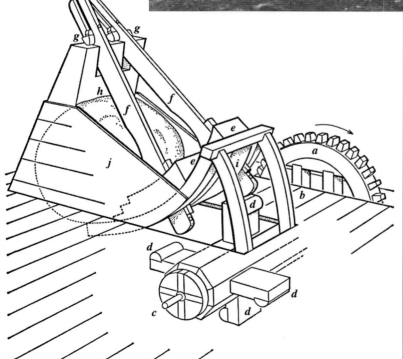

ABOVE: Fulling Trough. The Roman impluvium *found at Pompeii. BONECHI 1997*

Although the manufacture of the finished cloth was organised and carried on by its citizens, such as Chaucer's *'Wife of Bath'*, the monastery of Bath also played an important role in providing the material resources from its estates surrounding the city. This involved the leasing out of their mills to the fullers, as well as the provision of raw wool from their sheep 'ranches' on the Downs. Since the monastery also owned Southstoke, Monkton Combe and other manors on the south side of Bath, it can be assumed that it also provided the fuller's earth. Likewise, in the neighbouring parish of Wellow, the fuller's earth deposits there belonged to the Hungerfords of Farleigh, who also ran large sheep farms between their properties in Somerset and Wiltshire. Although the cloth trade was already moving out to the fulling mills in the countryside by the time of the Dissolution of the monastery in 1539, clothmaking was still carried on in Bath until the end of the 17th century and continued to flourish in the neighbouring parish of Twerton into the 20th century.

Brief references to fuller's earth in the Bath area first begin to appear in the early part of the 19th century. At this time, the fulling mills were supplied by farmers digging into landslips or from shallow pits and the Rev'd John Skinner, Rector of Camerton, recorded in his journal how the soil at Wellow was constantly being turned up by the clothiers in search of the earth. A more precise method of prospecting, however, was already being developed by William Smith (the Father of English Geology), who had acquired an intimate knowledge of the Fuller's Earth strata in the area whilst serving as sub-engineer for the construction of the Somersetshire Coal Canal in the 1790s. Indeed, he even bought the site of an old fulling mill at Tucking Mill, on the boundary of Monkton Combe and Southstoke, near which he built his own residence. It was from his experience of the geology around Bath that he was able to formulate his principles of stratigraphy, and foresee, in his *Prospectus* of 1801, how this would help identify fuller's earth and other valuable mineral deposits: '*Fullers, founders, glass makers etc. will learn where to send for earths and sands of the qualities best suited to their respective purposes.*' In that same year, Richard Warner wrote in his *The History of Bath* of '*the fuller's earth, which although but a thin stratum, is visible everywhere around Bath, by the slips on the declivities of the hills, occasioned by the springs of water which flow out of it.*' Ten years later, he included a map in his *A New Guide to Bath*, which showed fuller's earth within three miles of the city of Bath in the direction of Combe Hay, approximately where the works at Odd Down were developed at the end of the century. This may be the first record of an actual working.

There is a suggestion in Rees' *Cyclopaedia* of 1819, however, that fuller's earth mining was in decline by that time and Farey, in his article on fuller's earth in the *Cyclopaedia*, noted that '*the modern improvements in chemistry and the arts have rendered fuller's earth, of even the best quality, of comparatively small importance, to that which it had when particular statutes were judged necessary for prohibiting its exportation, under the severest penalties.*' This may be one of the reasons why the fulling mill at Stoney Littleton, near Wellow, was offered for sale in the *Bath Chronicle* in April 1803. Nevertheless, science was also beginning to discover that the clay had many other useful properties and, in 1822, it was stated that '*the fuller's earth of Combe Hay is said to have been much inquired for by foreign chemists.*' Even in the cloth industry, it was still found to be useful in the dyeing process to produce 'earthing', *i.e.* fastness to rubbing, since initially the new synthetic dyes were not resistant to soap or alkali in the treatment, for example, of brightly coloured blankets. Although some fuller's earth was still being mined from time to time at a number of locations to the south of Bath, such as Monkton Combe, Lyncombe & Widcombe, and, further west, Englishcombe and Duncorn Hill in the parish of Dunkerton, the Geological Survey of England and Wales Report of 1876, entitled *Geology of East Somerset and the Bristol Coalfields*, stated that '*shafts were formerly sunk in the fuller's earth south of Bath to a depth of 20 to 30 feet, with levels. It was then much used in fulling in the Cloth Mills at Frome and in Gloucestershire. It is however rarely if ever worked now in the district.*'

The 1880s were a time of useless rivalries between the various companies in the fuller's earth industry, bringing the price down to almost uneconomic levels. There had been a price war between the producers for the markets in those centres, notably Yorkshire, where woollen cloth was manufactured, even though the use of fuller's earth in the textile industry was declining. There were, however, new uses for the earth in the United States of America, with the recently patented methods for refining vegetable oils, including the decolourisation of glyceride oils about 1880. There was also a growing demand in the United States for the earth in the rapidly developing mineral oil-refining market. The demand for Richard Warner's '*useful earth*' had increased considerably, as new applications for it were

Richard Warner's 'Fossilogical Map of the Country five miles around Bath' published by him in A New Guide to Bath, *1811.*

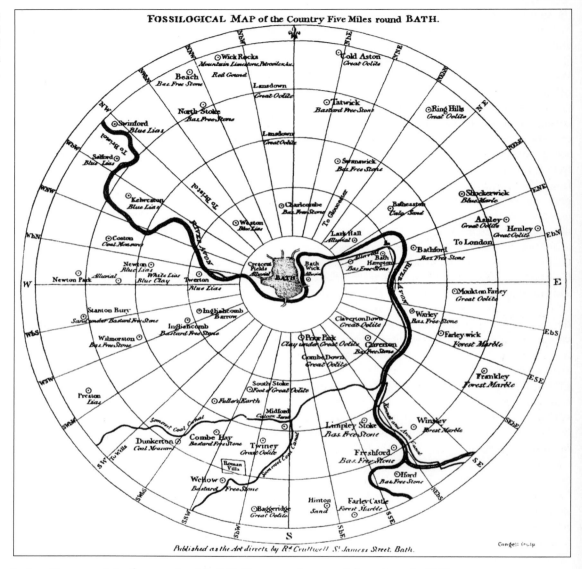

FOSSILOGICAL MAP of the Country Five Miles round BATH.

Published as the Act directs by R.ᵈ Cruttwell St James's Street, Bath.

Cangell Sculp.

being discovered. In the words of A.C.G. Cameron, in an article written in 1892:

'… it seems that by 1822 there was no great call for fuller's earth, the old cloth trade was beginning to decline and consequently a falling off in fuller's earth works was setting in. During more recent times the demand for this mineral fluctuated and decreased, its place being mainly supplied by soap and other chemical detergents. Of late years an unwontedly active demand has sprung up for it, and this continues to progress rapidly. The improvement is due, in no small degree, to the successful application of fuller's earth to the oil-refining business in America where there is an almost phenomenal demand for it.'

As the century drew towards a close, new pits on Rush Hill and at Combe Hay, Southstoke and Wellow were in operation and reports of the Bath & Western Highway Board in the 1870s stated that waggons carrying fuller's earth were causing damage to the roads in the parishes south of Bath. These mining ventures were all run by independent producers but, in 1887, Claude William Cawley from Surrey, who claimed to be responsible for half of the United Kingdom production, bought up the fuller's earth works at Wellow from F. Candy and, at Odd Down, from W.B. Hallett. The latter may well have been the Evergreen Works on Rush Hill. This company was known as Cawley & Co. Ltd. In March 1890, the Fullers' Earth Union was formed by merging the properties in Surrey and most of those in Somerset, with Cawley as the managing director and A.G.D. Moger as the first chairman. The Union then owned those that Cawley already held, together with Combe Hay, acquired from the Butler family, and that at Southstoke, from W.H. Handley. Two years later, Cawley was removed from office, possibly because he had problems with his new Somerset directors when Cawley & Co. had taken over their works and they had to resort to legal action in order to have their shares in the former company actually issued to them. The Union was really a cartel of parties interested in the marketing of the earth and it did not own all the producers until 1919.

A completely different company was founded in 1883 by George Dames, using a method of refining the earth patented by his brother Charles R. Dames. This company, known as The Midford Fuller's Earth Works Ltd (later owned by H.N. Garrett), was centred on Tucking Mill at Midford but did not become part of the Fullers' Earth Union until 1915. George Dames was the secretary of the Union when it was formed but he left the area shortly afterwards and subsequently sold to the Union the beds of fuller's earth which he either owned or leased at Midford. In the meantime, 1891 saw the establishment of what was to become the main fuller's earth works at Folly Down, on the southern outskirts of Bath, in the parish of Combe Hay. Owing to lack of demand, however, and despite all the efforts of the new company, profits were already declining when the world price plummeted in 1897 and thereafter, Cawley's original works in Surrey became the main producer in the United Kingdom. Nevertheless, production eventually recovered and such was the demand for fuller's earth, particularly during the Second World War, that it continued to be mined at Bath until 1980.

NOTES TO CHAPTER 1

In AD 47, the **Roman commander Ostorius Scapula** established his headquarters on a hill between Dunkerton and Wellow, to the south of Bath and near the Fosse Way. Details of the Combe Hay excavations from 1968 were published in the *SANHS Journal* in 1980.

The word **'fuller'** comes from the Latin *fullo*, 'a bath or laundry man, a preparer of cloth'. In a Roman villa, the *fullonica* was where the laundry was done. Both *fullonia* and *fullonica* are nouns derived from the adjectives *fullonius* and *fullonicus*, both of which mean 'related to a *fullo*, to what a *fullo* does'. Hence *fullonia* and *fullonica* could be 'a laundry, a *fullo's* place of work, a vat', *i.e.* referring to the trough in which the clothes were trampled in a suspension of fuller's earth in water.

The English **'Fuller's Earth'** is a translation of *terra fullonia*, an alternative term. *Terra* is a more general term 'earth or soil', whereas *creta* is 'clay, chalk or fine earth'.

In Roman times the collectors of stale urine from public places for fulling were known as *fulliones*.

'*Smectis*' was the first scientific name given to fuller's earth in Edward Phillips' dictionary of 1706. *Smektis* was used in classical Greek for fuller's earth, later writers used *smektris*. Associated words are *smektikos* (detergent) and *smegma* (soap), *smao* 'to wipe or cleanse with a soap or ointment', and a later form, *smecho*, 'to wipe off or wash off with the help of soap'. In medieval Bath, for example, the churchwardens of St Michael's parish used the Latin version of the word in 1425, when they paid 2d for soap to wash their new vestments – *Pro smygmate ad lavandum nova vestimenta iid.*

Fullers are referred to in the *Authorised Version* (King James Version) *of the Bible*. In the *Old Testament*, in *Malachi*, Chapter 3, verse 2, '*He is like a refiner's fire, and like fullers' soap.*' In the *New Testament*, in the *Gospel according to Mark*,

The Fullers' Teasel
Dipsacus sativus, *showing
the hooked spines which
make the head suitable for
raising the nap of cloth.*

Chapter 9, verse 3, says of Jesus that *'his raiment became shining, exceeding white as snow, so as no fuller on earth can white them.'* In *New Testament* Greek, the word used here for fuller is *gnapheus*, an alternative form of *knapheus*. It is defined as 'a fuller, cloth-dresser, clothes-cleaner', which in turn comes from the Greek word for the prickly **teasel** *knaphos*. This word also means a carding comb. Hence the verb *knapto* is 'to card or dress cloth, done with a teasel or with a comb'. The word 'nap', the woolly surface on cloth, may have been derived from this root. The Greek verb *knapheuo* (or *knapto*) was used for the laundering of woollen clothes rather than linen.

The **Fullers' Teasel** *Dipsacus sativus* is believed to be a sub species of *Dipsacus fullonum*, from which it differs only in the scales of the receptacle being hooked at the extremity, *i.e.* they end in a stiff recurved spine, which makes the heads suitable for raising the nap of certain kinds of cloth.

Teasel, or teazel, teazle, comes from the Old English *taesan* meaning 'to card, and hence to comb or raise the nap on cloth'. It is frequently mentioned in the churchwardens' accounts of St Michael's parish in Bath during the 15th century, where they were grown and sold to the local cloth trade, as indicated in the following extract and translation from 1459:

'Custos Ecclesie: Wm°. Galwyne pro delvynge et rydynge gardini ten¹ nuper Wm¹. Abyndone xii^d. Et eidem pro settynge dcc tesyll plontys iii^d. Et J¹. Wattys pro dict^s plontys iii^d. Et J¹. Strange pro wedynge de la tesyll in ten° nuper W¹. Abyndone iii^d.

Church expenses: To Wm. Galwyne for digging and clearing the garden of the tenement lately belonging to Wm. Abyndone, 12d. And to the same for setting 700 teasel plants, 3d. And to John Wattes for the said plants, 3d. And John Strange for weeding the teasel in the tenement lately belonging to Wm. Abyndone, 3d.'

To **tuck** means 'to dress, full or put on tenters', that is a frame with hooks for stretching the cloth. The word comes from the Old English *tucian* meaning 'to disturb, afflict', cf. the German word *zucken* to twitch.

Fuller's earth has also been known as '**Walker's** Earth' from the Old English *wealcere*, a fuller, because originally people walked on the wet cloth to full it by squeezing it, hence 'waulking'.

'To **felt**' means 'to mat the cloth' *i.e.* by matting the natural tendency of the fibres of wool to interlace and cling together is enhanced.

Chaucer (1340-1400) wrote of his vigorous and much-travelled West Country clothier, the 'Wife of Bath' in his *Canterbury Tales*:

'Of clooth-making she hadde swiche an haunt [skill],

She passed hem of Ypres and of Gaunt.'

By the early 17th century, most of the cloth workers in Bath lived in Broad Street and Walcot Street, in St Michael's parish, evidently the traditional centre of the city's cloth industry. The first known written record of fuller's earth in Somerset is at Mells, in Collinson's *History and Antiquities of the County of Somerset*, 1791. There is no mention of either Combe Hay or Englishcombe.

William Smith's Prospectus is dated '*At Midford, near Bath, June 1st, 1801*' and entitled '*Prospectus of a work entitled Accurate delineations and descriptions of the natural order of the various strata …*'

Farey's article in Rees' *Cyclopaedia* 1819 continued '*Fullers' earth has been deemed absolutely necessary to the well dressing of cloth; and hence foreigners, though they can procure wool to be clandestinely exported out of the kingdom, can never reach to the perfection of the English cloths &c without fullers' earth, which is very plentiful in England, and excels that of other countries in quality, as much as in quantity and cheapness. For this reason it is made a contraband commodity; and the export made equally criminal with that of exporting wool.*'

The *Cyclopaedia* described a **fulling mill**: Fulling Mill is a machine employed for washing, scouring, or fulling of cloth, either with a view of cleansing it, in which case it is termed scouring, or for the purpose of thickening woollen cloth, worsteds, &c, when it is termed milling. … *A fulling mill generally contains four, six, eight or ten pair of stocks, according to the quantity of work it is required to perform*; these are all moved by the same water wheel or steam engine; in the former case, the axis of the water wheel is employed to move two or three pairs, whilst the others receive their motion from one or two similar and parallel shafts, turned by cogwheels from the shaft of the water wheel. … *Levers or lifters, are fitted upon the shaft which alternately, as they pass the beaters, lift them up, and they descend by their own gravity; these beaters are formed from a large block of wood*, affixed to a long stem, moving on a centre which is supported at the top of the frame of the whole machine; the principal part of this is a large block of wood hollowed out into a large cavity for the reception of the cloth. This is termed the trough … pieces of wood [are] fixed to [it], and curved to a segment of a circle struck from the centre on which the beaters move. *In the spaces between these beams the stems of the beaters project so as to be intercepted by the lifters as they revolve.* The beaters are also curved at the lowest side to the same circle as the beams, so that they apply as close as possible to each other without touching. *This is necessary to prevent the cloth getting between them, and being pinched or cut thereby. The ends of the beaters, which act upon the cloth, are armed with three small boards, which project like teeth, and act more effectually to bend and disturb every portion of the cloth placed in the trough.* Boards are nailed to the block to form the sides of the trough and which also give strength to the machine. At one side these boards are not so high, for the convenience of taking the cloth out of the trough. *A supply of water, which hits a board so that it falls in a sheet, keeps the cloth constantly saturated.* FROM REES' CYCLOPAEDIA, VOL. XV, 1819

Cloth is placed in the 'box' of the machine against the *curved wooden breast* and is pounded by a pair of hammers which are lifted and released alternately by tappet wheels. *The 'feet' of the hammers are so shaped that the cloth is constantly turned.* When the machine is stopped, the hammers are held in the 'up' position by stangs, which are thrust into slots in the feet. FROM CHRIS ASPIN, THE WOOLLEN INDUSTRY, SHIRE BOOKS, 1982

The Rev'd **John Skinner** was Rector of Camerton 1803-34; the reference to Wellow is in his papers under Additional MS 33688 folio 29. Quoted in *Victoria County History* (see below)

References to fuller's earth begin to appear in official records around Bath in the 1840s:

1841 Census: Lewis Holloway, aged 20, listed as a fuller's earth miner living at Withyditch in the parish of Dunkerton
1846-7 Dunkerton Rate-book: Ann Perkins, rated for Fuller's Earth Mines – annual value £47.10.0 (one valued at £28.10.0)
1851 Census: John Holloway, listed as a fuller's earth miner, a visitor from Clutton, living in the parish of Dunkerton

The Rev'd **Richard Warner** (1763-1857) was an antiquarian and topographical writer who moved to this area in 1794 to become the officiating minister of St James's church in Bath. He immediately immersed himself in the history, environs and intellectual society of Bath, where he became a prominent figure and frequent correspondent in the *Bath Journal*. Warner's best-known work was his *History of Bath*, 1801, but he was also a prodigious writer on religious subjects and political reform, including several satyrs on local society. After acquiring curacies elsewhere at Great Chalfield and Chelwood he remained in the neighbourhood until his death. (DNB)

Sir Arthur **Conan Doyle's** sister was married to the Rector of Dunkerton, the Rev'd Gerard Ludlow Hallett (instituted 1874, rector until 1906), whom he visited. He probably would have known of the fuller's earth works on Odd Down as he journeyed from Bath to Dunkerton. In 1891-92, Conan Doyle wrote a Sherlock Holmes' story, *The Engineer's Thumb* which featured fuller's earth. The story contains the following quotation: '*Their land contained that which was quite as valuable as a gold mine*', referring to deposits of the earth in the south of England. The Rev'd Mr Hallett may have been related to W.B. Hallett, an owner of fuller's earth works on Odd Down.

BIBLIOGRAPHY

Anon., 'Fullers' Earth and the Roman Occupation', *Laporte News*, Vol. 8, No. 5, December 1969
Anon., 'Bath Mine - A Prehistoric Sandwich', (article in unknown Journal, c.1970s)
Behr, Nicholas von, 'The Cloth Industry of Twerton', *Bath History* Vol. VI, Millstream Books, Bath 1966
Bush, T.S., 'Churchwarden's Accounts, St Michael's, Bath', *Somerset Archaeology & Natural History Society Proceedings*, Vols 23, 25, 26; 1877, 1879, 1880
Cameron, A.C.G., *Proceedings of the Geological Association*, Vol. 12, p.395ff. Excursion to Woburn Sands and Sandy, 1892
Collinson, John, *The History and Antiquities of the County of Somerset*, 1791
Geological Survey of England and Wales Report, 1876, *Geology of East Somerset and the Bristol Coalfields*
Jenkins, D.T., and Ponting, K.G., *The British Wool Textile Industry 1770-1914*, Heinemann 1982
Ponting, K.G., *The West of England Cloth Industry*, Macdonald 1957
Ponting, K.G., 'Old Fulling Methods', *Journal of the Society of Dyers and Colourists*, Vol. 67, No. 11
Ponting, K.G., *Wool and Water*, 1975
Price, Rosalind, & Watts, Lorna, 'Rescue Excavations at Combe Hay 1968-73', *Somerset Archaeology & Natural History Society Proceedings*, Vol. 124, 1980
Rees, Abraham, *The Cyclopaedia or Universal Dictionary of Arts, Sciences & Literature*, Vol. XV, 1819
Robertson, R.H.S., *Fuller's Earth, A History of Calcium Montmorillonite*, Hyde, 1986
Rogers, K.H., *Wiltshire and Somerset Woollen Mills*, Pasold Research Fund 1976
Warner, Richard, *The History of Bath*, 1801
Warner, Richard, *A New Guide to Bath*, 1811, p.176f
Victoria County History of the Counties of England; Somerset, 1911; Vol. 1, p.23; Vol. 2, pp.353f, 419f

Diagrammatic section showing the correlation and lateral variation of the Bathonian between Bath and Frome.
AFTER KELLAWAY, G.A. & WELCH, F.B.A., BRITISH REGIONAL GEOLOGY, BRISTOL & GLOUCESTER DISTRICT, 1948

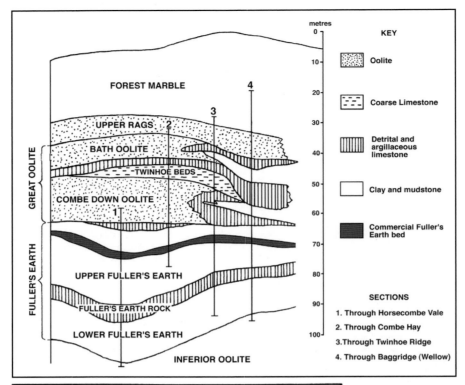

Lithological sequence and sampling levels in the Fuller's Earth Beds at Combe Hay Works on Odd Down, showing the probable appearance of the face in 1980.
CLAY MINERALS, 1986, 21, 293-310, MODIFIED AFTER JEANS ET AL., 1977

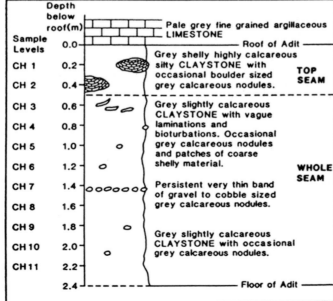

⊰🙢 **Chapter 2** 🙠⊱

'ALTHOUGH BUT A THIN STRATUM'
The Geology and Properties of Fuller's Earth

THE GEOLOGY OF FULLER'S EARTH

Some confusion arises from the fact that the phrase 'Fuller's Earth' is used in two different ways. The first use of the term is a geological one, being a description of a stratigraphical division in the strata of rocks and clays of the Middle Jurassic period. It was the eminent, early geologist William Smith who, in 1799, first applied the term 'Fuller's Earth' to the whole series of clays and impure limestones between the overlying freestone Great Oolite, used for building, and the underlying Inferior Oolite limestones.

The second use of the term is for a more specific bed of important economic fuller's earth within this whole series of clays, which occurs only in certain areas. In recent years, the term has been defined more rigorously as those clays which are rich in a chemical called calcium montmorillonite. The name derives from that applied by Maudyt in 1847, after the town of Montmorillon, some 42 miles north north west of Limoges in France. He simply stated that it contained silica, alumina and water. It is the presence of this calcium montmorillonite that produces the 'good fuller's earth' in the Bath area.

It is believed that this stratum, lying 60-80 feet (18-24m) below the surface, was laid down some 160 million years ago in the Jurassic period, having originated in volcanic ash, rich in mica, possibly from a volcano off the Cornish coast. This ash settled in shallow lagoons and seas, and became eventually what we know today as commercial fuller's earth. Over the years, there has been much discussion as to how the fuller's earth was formed but, according to a report of the Institute of Geological Sciences in 1978, there seems to be:

> *'little doubt of the volcanic material but the mode of deposition and the source of the ash is still speculative. It could be vitric ash which was argillised, or changed into a clay, in situ, the ash being deposited in a shallow water environment ... it certainly cannot be a single primary ashfall deposit. It is more likely to be a reworking of water deposited ash. The ultimate source of the ash probably lay to the west of Great Britain'.*

William Lonsdale, who became the first curator of the Bath Royal Literary & Scientific Institution in 1825, divided Smith's Fuller's Earth formation into four sections. Starting from the top there is some 30-40 feet of blue or yellow clay with nodules of marl, below which there is a 'top seam' of some 3-5 feet of 'bad' fuller's earth. This layer has a low calcium montmorillonite content but is rich in calcite or crystalline calcium carbonate. Below these layers there is the 'main or lower seam', which contained a band some 2.5-3 feet of 'good' blue or brown fuller's earth. This layer has a high calcium montmorillonite and low calcite content. Finally, there is a much thicker seam of 100 feet of clay with 'bad' fuller's earth and nodular limestone marl. Lonsdale commented that *'the good fuller's earth is confined to the brow of Odd Down and the side of Midford Hill.'* Joseph Sutcliffe had written in 1822 *'At Coombe Hay there is a vein of fuller's earth; and, no doubt, the like veins occur in other parts of the country, if the well-sinkers did but know them.'* These were later to prove to be the most productive local areas for

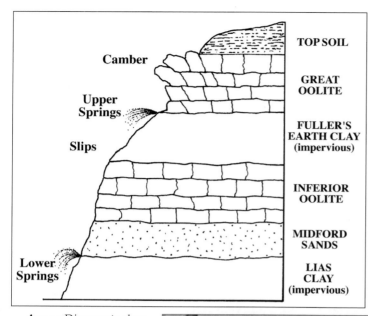

TOP SOIL

Camber

GREAT
OOLITE

Upper
Springs

FULLER'S
EARTH CLAY
(impervious)

Slips

INFERIOR
OOLITE

MIDFORD
SANDS

Lower
Springs

LIAS
CLAY
(impervious)

*ABOVE: Diagram to show
the emission of springs,
cambering and slippage due
to rain water.*

*RIGHT: William Smith's
House at Tucking Mill,
showing the original part
on the western side. The
memorial tablet to William
Smith was originally
placed on the mill and
transferred to Tucking
Mill Cottage when the mill
was demolished, not on
this house. (See Chapter
4 for other illustrations of
Smith's house.)*
ALEC PALMER

mining the earth at the end of the 19th century.

Another geological feature connected with fuller's earth is that springs of water, known locally as the 'Upper Springs', appear at the top of the seam, *i.e.* at the junction of the porous limestone and the impenetrable clays. The usual causes of many local landslips seen on the hills around Bath are due to water percolating over the slippery clays of the fuller's earth and bringing the overlying beds of rock down the slope.

William Smith achieved considerable fame for his work in stabilising land in the Bath area that was prone to slipping. At Combe Grove, at the top of Brassknocker Hill, he was able to stop landslipping by tunnelling into the hillside to intercept the ground water. Hugh Torrens has suggested that the sinking of the famous hydrostatic caisson lock at Combe Hay, on the Somersetshire Coal Canal circa 1799, through layers of fuller's earth may have been responsible for its failure. Joan Eyles has pointed out that 1799 was a particularly wet year and that, although the caisson lock had been demonstrated in April, the following month the Committee decided that it had to be rebuilt because it was leaking. When the fuller's earth became water logged, it would have swollen and exerted pressure on the stone walls of the cistern causing it to become distorted and so fail. Knowing the damage caused by the fuller's earth clay to the Sapperton Tunnel on the Thames & Severn Canal, William Smith may have already recognised that the cistern had been excavated in a geologically unstable spot and the suspicion remains that this may have been the issue in April, when his engagement as sub-engineer on the canal was terminated. Hedgemead Park, on the north side of Bath, was laid out in 1889 following a series of landslips from 1865 onwards. This culminated in the demolition of 135 houses in 1881. The land was clearly unsuitable for rebuilding, possibly due to the presence of fuller's earth in that area.

True fuller's earth was found when the Box Tunnel was driven in 1841 and also exposed in the cuttings near Midford during the construction of the Somerset & Dorset Joint Railway between 1872-74. Eventually, the most significant mining of fuller's earth occurred at the southern end of Odd Down in the parish of Combe Hay, at Wellow, the top of the hill from Midford into Bath, at Hodshill in Southstoke, on

Rush Hill in Odd Down and in the parish of Englishcombe. Other pits, where the earth was obtained from landslips or from shallow exposures, have been recorded as being at Lyncombe and Widcombe, Claverton Down, Monkton Combe, Duncorn Hill and Dunkerton.

THE CHEMISTRY OF FULLER'S EARTH, ITS STRUCTURE AND FORMULA

In the 1930s, the American Nobel prize winning chemist Linus Pauling determined the chemical structure of montmorillonite, which belongs to the class of minerals known as the alumino-silicates, and this marked the start of the modern understanding of the structure of the clays. As a result, the chemical structure of calcium montmorillonite, the active constituent of fuller's earth, may best be thought of as a lattice or three-dimensional grid. This lattice has three sheets, consisting of one aluminium hydroxyl unit sandwiched between two sheets of linked silicon oxide (Si_4O_{10}). The sheets are linked by oxygen atoms common to both. The basic building block is the silicon tetrahedron SiO_4, i.e. a silicon atom at the centre with one oxygen atom at each of the four corners. These link up to form a silica sheet and are attached to similar sheets formed from aluminium hydroxyl units. The result is a complex chemical compound with the theoretical formula $Al_4(Si_4O_{10})_2(OH)_4nH_2O$, where nH_2O is the hygroscopic water content. In fact, the molecule always differs from this because of the substitutions of other elements which can take place within the lattice. The aluminium can be partly or wholly replaced by ferric iron, magnesium, zinc and other elements, and the silicon can be partly replaced by aluminium.

The sheets are stacked in layers, rather like lasagne, with water molecules between the layers accounting for the variable quantity of water in the earth. The distance between the layers can vary from 9.6 angstrom units in the dehydrated form to 21.4 angstrom units when the mineral is water saturated. Montmorillonite is therefore said to have an expanding lattice which is reversible. This explains the landslips in the Bath area referred to above.

Montmorillonite has a silicon:aluminium ratio of about 2:1 and it seems that other cations such as magnesium and iron are essential to its formation. The three-layer unit has a net negative charge resulting from these substitutions. This charge deficiency is balanced by exchangeable cations adsorbed between the unit layers and around the edges of the molecule, the most usual of these cations being calcium and sodium. The calcium atoms in the naturally occurring calcium montmorillonite can be detached under suitable chemical reactions and replaced with sodium ones, a process known as ion-exchange. The chemical composition of montmorillonite is therefore exceedingly variable and complex. There are many complications in the mixture, both mechanically and in 'mixed' crystals and the clay particles, which range from crystalline through imperfect crystals to amorphous or gel states.

The unique properties of natural fuller's earth are due to its high surface area of approximately 95 square yards (80 sq. m) per gramme, which weight for weight, is far greater than that of other minerals. This extensive surface area, the ability of water to penetrate between the sheets of the montmorillonite and the porosity of fuller's earth give it powerful absorbent properties and hence its use in pharmacy and household cleaners. The above figure rises to 300 square metres when the earth is treated with a mineral acid. This process was not used at Bath as the presence of calcite, i.e. crystalline calcium carbonate, in all parts of the local seams made it unsuitable for acid activation.

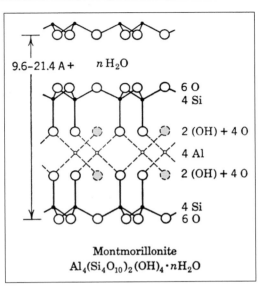

9.6–21.4 A + $n H_2O$

6 O
4 Si

2 (OH) + 4 O

4 Al

2 (OH) + 4 O

4 Si
6 O

Montmorillonite
$Al_4(Si_4O_{10})_2(OH)_4 \cdot nH_2O$

Structure of Montmorillonite. The structure has layers consisting of one aluminium-hydroxyl unit sandwiched between two (Si_4O_{10}) sheets. These layers are stacked one above the other in the vertical direction, with water molecules between them. The variable water content accounts for the expansion of the molecule from 9.6Å in the dehydrated state to 21.4Å when the mineral is water saturated. Montmorillonite is therefore said to have an expanding lattice structure. AFTER MACEWAN, D.M.C, X-RAY IDENTIFICATION AND CRYSTAL STRUCTURE OF CLAY MINERALS (MIN. SOC.) 2ND ED.; ALSO GRIM, R.E., IN J. GEOL, 1942

Fuller's earth can be compared to a 'chemical sponge'. From its physical structure, and the 'active' sites on the large surface, the earth derives its extraordinary powers of attaching other substances to it by absorption and adsorption. It has the ability to absorb within its molecular structure the molecules of other substances. Furthermore it is able to adsorb on its surface molecules of other foreign substances. Among the types of molecule most easily attached to it are those which give plant and animal matter their colour, hence its traditional bleaching properties. It is this ability to soak up water, grease, oil and colour that distinguishes it from many other clays and hence it has been used since classical times for the fulling or whitening of textiles. It is also capable of adjoining particles of fuller's earth to itself.

There are different theories as to the decolourising ability of the earth. It is helped by using purer clay. It does seem certain that the crystal structure, cleavage, adsorption ability, base-exchange capacity and the chemical composition give certain clay materials, notably montmorillonite, the property of decolourising oils or permit them to be activated so that they gain this ability to decolourise. The decolourising of glyceride oils is best with 4-6% moisture content in the earth and it seems that some water is necessary to allow cation exchange to take place. This bleaching power is impaired when the moisture reaches or exceeds eight water molecules. At Bath, the moisture content of natural fuller's earth is 34-36% on a calcite free basis. In suspension, the particles form a gel which, on agitation, becomes a highly viscous liquid and is of great importance in the oil drilling industry.

When the natural earth is treated with soda ash, anhydrous sodium carbonate, a process that was used on some of the earth at Bath, the calcium is replaced with sodium. This alters the properties of the earth for different industrial and commercial uses and is an example of ion-exchange. The product so formed is a swelling clay similar to the naturally occurring Bentonite with exceptional bonding power.

THE PHYSICAL CHARACTERISTICS OF FULLER'S EARTH

As mined, fuller's earth is soft, greasy, grey-blue or yellow in colour but weathers to buff or brown. Yellow fuller's earth may be due to oxidation of the earth which lies above the water table. The unweathered material fractures like hard wax. In water, it falls to a powder and does not have the plastic properties of other clays. When shaken with an excess of water it swells to many times its original volume before breaking down to a soapy paste or mud and it can adsorb water up to eight times its original volume.

Sutcliffe, writing in 1822, stated that *'the exterior colour is not dissimilar to the Hampshire and Bedfordshire earths; but the interior exhibits a dull blue, like the blue clouded parts of white lias … it dissolves quickly in water, and coagulates, if the water is slightly mixed with acids.'* Woodward observed in 1893 that the surface water drained off the sediment pits in Somerset was said to be very soft, pure and drinkable. Possibly he was referring to water from the settling tanks at Tucking Mill.

Dry earth is porous, the pores being indicated by the escape of many air bubbles when a fragment is immersed in a liquid. The total porosity is probably increased by the random orientation of the montmorillonite flakes. The layers of molecular water which occur between the aluminium-silicon sheet units may be driven off on heating the mineral, which then swells greatly on being mixed again with water, a property which gives it important uses in oilfield work.

The bed of Bath's commercial fuller's earth varies in thickness from 6-10 feet (2-3m) throughout the area and has a moisture content, when mined, of approximately 33%, which was dried to 6% for the foundry and pharmaceutical industries. The upper part of the seam is gritty, due to a higher calcite content of 20-45%; this was Lonsdale's 'bad fuller's earth'. This earth was dried to about 3% moisture and sold as a carrier for fertilisers and a binder for cattle foods. The lower third of the seam had only an 18% calcite content. 'All Best' was the whole seam after calcite nodules and boulders had been removed. The mixed product has approximately 22% calcium carbonate and the purest samples obtained from the Bath seams had less than 5%.

NOTES TO CHAPTER 2

Richard Warner wrote in his *The History of Bath*, 1801:

*'the fuller's earth which, although but a thin stratum, is visible everywhere round Bath, by the slips on the declivities of the hills, occasioned by the **springs** of water which flow out of it. This is followed by a very deep bed of imperfect or bastard's fuller's earth …'*

Robert Weldon's experimental 'Hydrostatick' or **Caisson Lock**, built at Combe Hay on the Somersetshire Coal Canal between 1796-1800, enabled a boat to be lifted vertically through 46 feet. Three of these were planned to overcome the 135 feet drop between the two levels of the canal. The boat was floated into a sealed wooden vessel (the caisson) submerged in a water-filled masonry cistern. Because the caisson was ballasted to be weightless, it could therefore be easily raised or lowered by hand without the loss of any water. When it eventually failed, it was finally replaced in 1805 by a flight of 22 conventional locks.

Calcite or Iceland Spar is calcium carbonate in the crystalline form.

Bentonite named from Fort Benton, Rock Creek, Wyoming, USA (*Dictionary of Geology*, J. Challinor)

Soda Ash is anhydrous sodium carbonate in powder form. It is produced when sodium carbonate (washing soda) is heated to drive off the water of crystallisation and is also known as 'calcined soda'.

Adsorption – the drawing in of liquids into the pores of a solid.

Absorption – the attraction of a substance from a solution or vapour to the surface of a particle. Robertson comments on the absorption of liquids *i.e.* the ability of water to penetrate between the sheets. The porosity of fuller's earth means that it has powerful absorption powers and hence has found use in household cleaners, pharmacy, industrial floor cleaning and cat litter. Again he says that examples of its property of adsorption from solutions are very numerous *e.g.* in purifying beverages, glucose and molasses, and in the removal of the bitter taste from some fruit juices and dyes.

1 **Angstrom** unit = 10^{-10}metres or 10,000 microns

Linus C. Pauling (1901-1994). He studied in Europe between 1925 and 1927 and this included working in England with Sir William Bragg, whose special field was crystallography. Pauling's early work was the study of molecular structures. During the decade 1930-40, he was acknowledged as the father of modern chemistry. From 1957, he organised 11,000 scientists world-wide against nuclear testing. He was a great believer in the efficacy of vitamin C, which he took in large daily doses! He was a double Nobel Prize winner, the only one to be awarded twice on his own, for chemistry in 1954, and for peace in 1962. He died on 19th August 1994 at the age of 93.

Woodward in 1894 gives the following **analysis** of earth from the Midford pits at the top of Horsecombe Vale:

Chemical	Blue %	Yellow %
Silica	54.0	59.3
Alumina	18.6	20.8
Ferric oxide	3.9	4.2
Ferrous oxide	0.8	-
Lime	7.0	2.5
Magnesia	2.3	1.9
Soda	0.7	0.6
Potash	1.8	1.7
Carbonic acid	3.4	0.3
Loss by ignition	7.2	8.6
TOTAL	99.7	99.9

Jeans *et alia* gave the following figures obtained by Laporte Industries at their Combe Hay mine about 1975:

Height above base of seam	3 ft	6 ft
Chemical	%	%
Silicon oxide	58.8	59.7
Aluminium oxide	20.9	21.5
Ferric oxide	5.1	5.1
Magnesium oxide	2.7	2.7
Calcium oxide	2.0	2.2
Sodium oxide	0.5	0.6
Potassium oxide	2.3	2.6
TOTAL	92.3	94.4

BIBLIOGRAPHY

Anon., 'Fuller's Earth', *Bulletin of the Imperial Institute*, 1924

Arkell, W.J., & Donovan, D.T., 'The Fuller's Earth of the Cotswolds and its relation to the Great Oolite', *Quarterly Journal of the Geological Society of London*, 1952

Blunden, J., *The Mineral Resources of Britain*, Hutchinson 1975

Cook, D.A., 'Investigation of a landslip in the fuller's earth clay, Lansdown, Bath', *Quarterly Journal of Engineering Geology*, Vol. 6, 1973

Eyles, Joan.M., 'William Smith: Some Aspects of his Life & Work', *Towards a History of Geology*, MIT Press 1969

Fuller, Dr. John G.C.M., 'The Industrial Basis of Stratigraphy, John Strachey 1671-1743 and William Smith 1769-1839', *American Association of Petroleum Geologists Bulletin*, Vol. 53, No. 11, 1969

Green, G.W. & Donovan, J., 'The Great Oolite Series of the Bath Area', *Bulletin of the Geological Survey*, 30, 1969

Hallam, A., & Selwood, B.W., 'Origins of Fuller's Earth in the Mezoic of Southern England', *Nature*, Vol. 220, London 1968

Hawkins, A.B., 'Jurassic Rocks of the Bath Area', in *Geological Excursions in the Bristol District*, ed. Savage, R.J.G., University of Bristol 1977

Hawkins, A.B., Lawrence, M.S., & Privett, K.D., 'Clay Mineralogy and Plasticity of the Fuller's Earth Formation, Bath', *Clay Minerals* 21, 1986

Highley, D.E., *Fuller's Earth*, (Mineral Dossier No.3), Mineral Resources Consultative Committee Institute of Geological Sciences HMSO, 1972

'Fuller's Earth 1913-1919', *The Mineral Industry of the British Empire & Foreign Countries*, Imperial Mineral Resources Bureau 1920

Jeans, C.V., Merriman, R.J., & Mitchell, J.G., 'Origins of the Middle Jurassic', *Clay Minerals*, Vol. 12, 1976

Kellaway, G.A. & Welch, F.B.A., *British Regional Geology, Bristol & Gloucester District*, HMSO 1957

Kellaway, G.A. & Taylor, J.H., *Influence of landslipping on the development of the City of Bath*, 23rd International Geological Congress, 1968, Vol. 12

Kerr, P.F., 'Montmorillonite or Smectite as constituents of Fuller's Earth or Bentonite', *American Minerals*, Vol. 17, 1932

Kerr, P.F., & Hamilton, P.K., 'Glossary of Clay Mineral Names', *American Petroleum Institute Research Project 49 Prelim.Report* No. 1, 1949

Lonsdale, William, 'On the Oolite District of Bath', *Transactions of the Geological Society*, Vol. III, London 1832

Mason, B., *Principles of Geochemistry*, 3rd edn, John Wiley & Sons 1966

Moorlock, B.S., & Highley, D.E., 'An Appraisal of Fuller's Earth Resources in England & Wales', *British Geological Survey Technical Report*, 1991

Newton, E.F., 'Petrography of Fuller's Earth Deposits', *Economic Geology*, 1934

Newton, E.F., 'The Petrography of some English Fuller's Earth and the Rocks associated with them', Proc. Geological Association, 1937

Penn, I.E., Wyatt, R.J., & Merriman, R.J., 'The Bathonian Strata of the Bath-Frome Area', *Institute of Geological Sciences Report*, Vol. 22, 1978

Penn, I.E., Wyatt, R.J., Morgan, D.J., & Merriman, R.J., *Fuller's earth provings near Baggridge, Avon*, Institute of Geological Sciences, Southern England & South Wales Land Survey Division 1978

Phillips, J.A., *Memoir of William Smith*, John Murray 1844

Phillips, J.A., *Memoirs of William Smith*. Additional material by H.S. Torrens, Bath Royal Literary & Scientific Institution 2003

Richardson, L, 'On a Fuller's Earth Section at Combe Hay near Bath', *Proceedings of the Geological Association*, Vol. XXI, 1910

Robertson, R.H.S., Tessier, D., & White, J.L., 'The Texture of an English Fuller's Earth', *Clay Minerals*, Vol.17, 1982

Sheppard, T., Article on William Smith, *Proceedings of Yorkshire Geological Society*, Vol. 19, 1917

Sutcliffe, J., *Geology of the Avon*, 1822

Torrens, H.S., 'Some Fuller's Earth sections in the South Cotswolds' *Proc. Bristol Nat. Hist. Soc.*, Vol. 31, 1968

Torrens, H.S., 'Somersetshire Coal Canal Caisson Lock', *Bristol Industrial Archaeology Society Journal*, Vol. 8, 1975

Warner, Richard, *The History of Bath*, 1801

Warner, Richard, *A New Guide to Bath*, 1811

Wells, C., *Fuller's Earth*, J.B. Lippincott & Co., 1932

Winchester, Simon, *The Map that Changed the World*, 2001, Viking-Penguin

Winwood, H.H., 'Geology', in *Handbook to Bath*, Pitman 1888

Woodward, H.B., Memoirs of the Geological Survey England & Wales, *Geology of East Somerset & the Bristol Coalfields*, HMSO 1876

Woodward, H.B., Memoirs of the Geological Survey of the United Kingdom, *The Jurassic Rocks of Britain*, Vol. IV, HMSO 1894

Wyatt, R.J. & Merriman, R.J., 'The Fuller's Earth deposits at Combe Hay, near Bath', *Guide for Field Excursion E5 International Clay Conference*, 1978

Chapter 3

PIONEERS IN HORSECOMBE VALE

The Top Works, Incline and Pan, 1883-1945

INTRODUCTION

Lonsdale was right. There was a good bed of fuller's earth three miles from the centre of Bath at the top of Midford Hill. It was probably these deposits that George Dames leased from the Midford Castle estate in 1883, when his brother Charles Richard Dames patented a novel method of refining fuller's earth, *'freeing it of all extraneous matter'*. The object of the process was to extract moisture, shells, stones and insoluble lime from the earth. The enterprise consisted of three distinct parts – the mining at the top of Horsecombe Vale, the breaking down of the clods of earth at the bottom of the valley and the final refining at Tucking Mill.

The report of the Bath Field Club in 1888 contained the passage:

'The Fuller's Earth industry having lately been much developed in our locality, new excavations have recently been made on the North side of the hill on which Midford Castle is situated, and a driving of some length on the horizon of the Fuller's Earth, here about 20 feet thick. Several visits were paid by the Secretary (the Rev'd H.H.Winwood) from time to time to the works in company with Mr H.B. Woodward, of the Geological Survey (1887) and others, and specimens of the Blue Clays and Yellow Earth were sent up to Professor Rupert Jones who was engaged in a microscopical examination of such clays.'

Bladud, 'The Bath Society Paper', referring to Horsecombe Vale in 1887, noted that:

'… long excavations have taken place on the brow of the further hill, and a snorting steam engine at the bottom of the hollow gives evidence, by its unromantic presence, of the pitiless march of progress. It was in 1883 that Mr C.R. Dames invented a process for the cleaning and refining of fuller's earth, and a large deposit of that substance having been discovered near the summit of the hill in question, a company was formed for the purpose of working it.'

A contemporary description of the process in Horsecombe Vale was included in the *Victoria History of Somerset* and other publications:

'The raw earth is conveyed in trucks to a pug-mill, where it is ground up with about three times its bulk in water. The 'slurry' thus produced is turned into little tanks or catch pits where the fine fuller's earth remains in a state of suspension, the coarse sinking to the bottom. It is then run into long earthenware drains underground to the works, in some cases half a mile distant.'

THE MINES

The adits, between 4 to 6 feet high (1.2-1.8m), were driven under the road towards the south; one had its entrance supported by masonry. An underground plan, which dates from 1888 but shows earlier workings, indicates that the mines extended over 15 to 20 acres (6 to 8 ha) under the

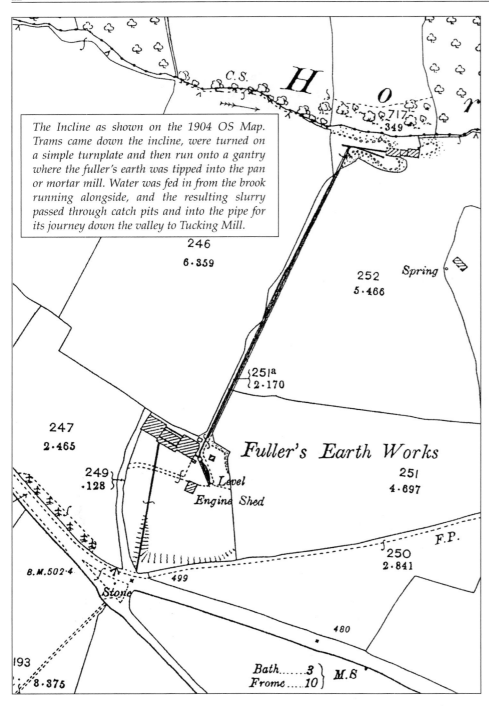

The Incline as shown on the 1904 OS Map. Trams came down the incline, were turned on a simple turnplate and then run onto a gantry where the fuller's earth was tipped into the pan or mortar mill. Water was fed in from the brook running alongside, and the resulting slurry passed through catch pits and into the pipe for its journey down the valley to Tucking Mill.

fields recorded on the 1840 Tithe map as Combe Land, Henleys, Milestone Ground, Little Breach and Packhorse Ground. These were all situated around the junction of the Old Midford Road with the present Midford Road. A drying shed near the adits was used as the datum level for the underground measurements. The plan was kept up to date until 1st August 1914 but was not continued by the Fullers' Earth Union when it took over the business the following year.

To the west of the incline, which connected the mines with the pug-mill, there were two adits, possibly more. A further two adits were on the east side with the remains of an embankment, which is still visible today. There were two air shafts at the end of the workings, to the south of Packhorse Lane. At weekends, the horses used in the adits were taken down to graze beside the pug-mill – an echo of Saxon times, when 'Horscum', meaning 'a valley in which horses were pastured', was included in a charter of 961 by King Edgar granting Southstoke to the Abbey at Bath.

Mining continued at the top of Horsecombe Vale after the Fullers' Earth Union took over but around the end of 1918, excavation had been suspended, probably because the heading was dangerous and it was unsafe for men to work underground. Owen Keevil, the local manager, realised that a new heading was required. As an interim measure, he therefore aimed at getting 100 tons of wet earth being brought each week from Combe Hay by the Yorkshire steam traction engine, always referred to as the 'steam waggon'. This would have been let down the inclines and slurried at the pug-mill.

In 1919 Keevil reported that 337 feet (103m) of the main adit needed re-timbering and that they had encountered the geological Somerset Great Fault. It extended from Midford to Priston and the miners would have to cut down 20 feet (6m) through solid freestone. When the earth was found again, they would have to ascend a steep slope or 'dipple'. The seam of fuller's earth at this lower level could not be followed without steam winding and a pumping plant to cope with the flooding then present, which could cost between £500 and £800. His father, W.F. Keevil, formerly manager at Combe Hay but by then based at Redhill, reported to the board of the Fullers' Earth Union that he believed it was uneconomical to continue mining at this site as enough earth was being obtained from Combe Hay. It was necessary, however, to keep an eye on the adit so that it did not collapse under the Midford Road!

One of the Horsecombe Vale adits, known as the Day Level.
FROM THE GEOLOGICAL SURVEY

It is therefore not surprising to find that mining in the valley was finally abandoned in 1920-21, as it had become uneconomical to upgrade the workings and continue extracting the earth. There had been accidents in the adits when some of the tunnels caved in. Ivor Stephens remembered that, when he was a boy in the 1920s, one of the adits had fallen in. The *List of Mines in Great Britain* (HMSO 1922) states *'Midford at Southstoke abandoned 1921'*.

THE TOP WORKS

The development of 'Southstoke Works', or 'Top Works' as it was usually called, is unclear from 1883 until they were no longer used during the 1920s. The works were sited near the top of Horsecombe Vale, a few yards below the Midford Road on approximately the same level as one of the adits. The 1904 map shows a short incline leading from the road down to the works, where there was an engine house and the entrance to a single adit. The corrugated iron buildings included a drying shed, in which some of the earth from the mine was dried and may then have been taken up the incline to the road for despatch. The records show that drying was stopped here, temporally, in December 1918, as there was a surplus of dry earth. The greater bulk of the wet earth was let down the much longer incline that began at the works and descended to the Pan Grinding Works, which contained the pug-mill, at the bottom of the valley. The boiler would therefore have been needed for drying the earth and to haul the tramway wagons, known as 'trams', out of the adits, and later for the machinery which powered the incline. In a letter dated June 1919 to James Palmer, the works foreman at Tucking Mill, Owen Keevil said he wanted 12 tons of blue earth ground at the Pan. At that time they were also grinding Black Clay. As there are no other references to grinding at the actual Pan, the question arises as to whether there was a mill at the Top Works, which could grind earth mined and dried there, or sent from Combe Hay.

The Southstoke builder O.J. Dobson was employed in August 1914 to carry out repairs to the winding pulley wheel and the roof for the wet earth, and to concrete the loading shed floor. By the time the Fullers' Earth Union took over in July 1915, most of the plant was in a very run down state and in September, Owen Keevil wrote a report for the board of the company on the equipment

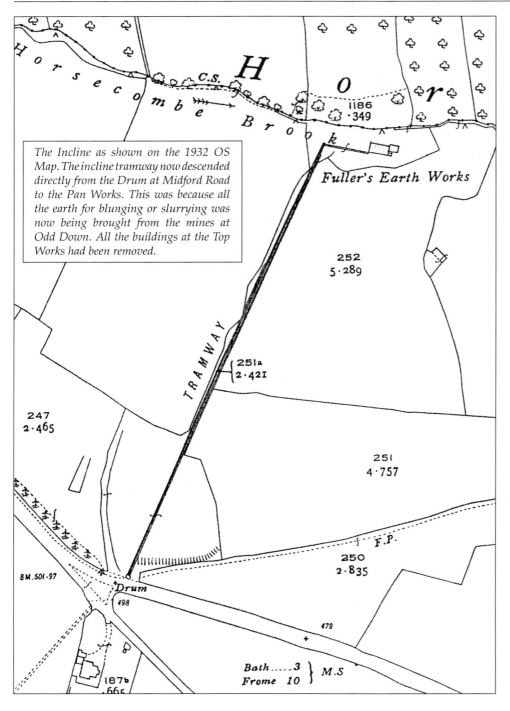

The Incline as shown on the 1932 OS Map. The incline tramway now descended directly from the Drum at Midford Road to the Pan Works. This was because all the earth for blunging or slurrying was now being brought from the mines at Odd Down. All the buildings at the Top Works had been removed.

and machinery it had inherited. Most of it was described as being in a poor state, needing either repair or replacement. The boilers and machinery at the Top Works were in bad condition and the winding machinery had been condemned by their insurance company. The engine there was described as being very old and wasteful of steam.

A programme of modernisation was started. A new Davey Paxman boiler was installed that year and a new Griffin engine was to be brought from the Combe Hay works, to be supplied with steam from the boiler. This engine was made by the Bath firm, The Griffin Engineering Company. Keevil also arranged for deliveries of coal, bags and timber, as there was apparently none in stock, and for telephones to be installed at Tucking Mill and Top Works.

Around 1917, Mark Barrett, the blacksmith who lived in the cottage opposite the Cross Keys Inn on the Midford Road, was called in to repair the wooden winding drum and to construct a pipe from the engine room to the loading sheds, presumably at the Top Works. He was also asked to supply eight wooden trams. In August 1917, Dobson was asked to construct a paraffin tank at the engine house for the sum of £2.10s (£2.50) and the following May he was busy building a loading shed at the Top Works.

By the time the 1932 map was published, all traces of the Top Works buildings had disappeared and the tramway had been realigned so that it now ran directly from the roadside, where it was marked 'Drum', to the Pan works. This is the gravity tramway that many people remember. As no mining now took place in Horsecombe Vale, all the earth was brought from the Combe Hay excavations and let down to the Pan in side-tipping trams, to be slurried as before. Hamlen, a local haulier, was able to transport 7-ton loads from Combe Hay because the gradients were fairly level between the two sites. This practice was to continue for some thirty years until the end of the Second World War.

THE INCLINES

According to the article in *Bladud*, the earliest arrangement consisted of a double line of rails which ran down the side of the steep hill to the Pan and provided a self acting incline; the descending loaded trams pulled up the empty ones and the connecting rope passed round a drum at the top. The 1904 map also shows a short incline between the road and the Top Works worked on the gravity principle. Lynn Willies has pointed out the importance of this incline as the lane down from Midford Road was very steep and clayey, and it would not have been easy for a horse and cart or for the steam lorry to negotiate. This incline would have been used to bring coal, wood and any other materials to the Top Works. Later, wet fuller's earth from Combe Hay was brought in and dried earth taken out by this method.

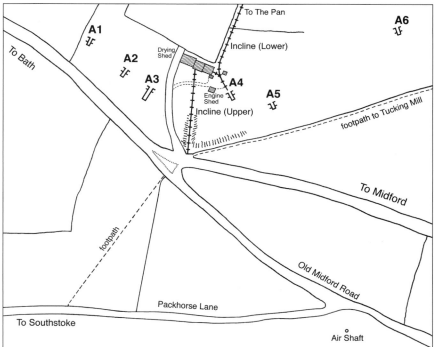

Early in the 20th century, this system is believed to have been replaced by an engine operating the drum and cable. According to Robertson, a new engine was installed in 1904, which was also used to pull trams from the adit close to the works. One set of rails led into the sheds and the other onto the longer incline. Later, there were two winding drums mounted on girders at the top of the incline and powered by the steam engine. The two sets of trams were coupled in groups of three on the incline.

In 1918, Owen Keevil wanted a second winding drum at the top of the incline where the wet earth from Combe Hay was tipped – but where exactly was this? Was it at the roadside, the site of the 'Drum' on the later map, or at the Top Works where the lower incline began? Just after this, Keevil said that he believed that the tyres on the Yorkshire steam waggon were being cut by the old steam kiln plates, which had been laid down at Top Works to form a base for shovelling the earth. In that year, some six loads of earth were being sent each week to be let down and slurried.

From the Top Works, the mined earth was let down this 720 feet (220m) long, steeply inclined tramway to the bottom of Horsecombe Vale some 150 feet (45m) below, the rope passing round a large drum. In 1920, when a new wire rope was ordered, it was to be 290 yards (265m) long and half inch (12.7mm) diameter. The length was to be measured from the Drum to where the trams stopped at the Pan. The men were instructed to lock up the trams, either on the incline or get them into the wet earth shutes at the Pan, every Saturday after the work of slurrying was finished for the week.

Top Works Adits. These are marked on the 1904 OS map and when examined in 1992, showed that Adit No. 1 had a stone arch over the entrance, No. 2 had completely collapsed, whilst No. 3 was most impressive, with stone embankments leading to the entrance to the adit.

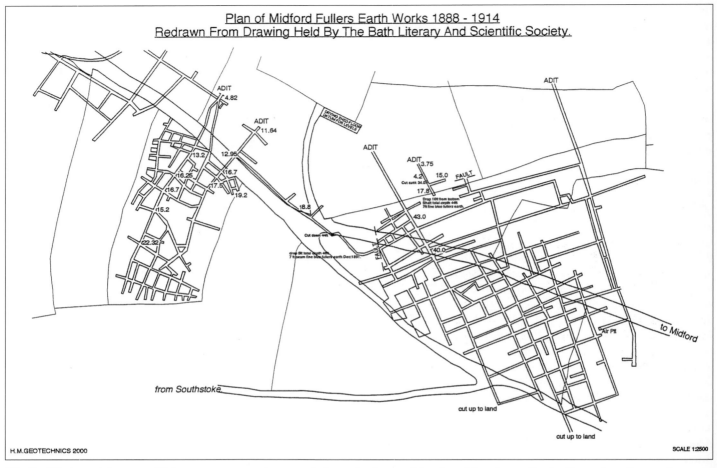

Plan of Midford Fullers Earth Works 1888 - 1914
Redrawn From Drawing Held By The Bath Literary And Scientific Society.

H.M.GEOTECHNICS 2000

SCALE 1:2500

The Top Works and the area excavated c.1888-1914. Although excavating took place for a few years after the Fullers' Earth Union acquired the mine from H.N. Garrett (Bath) Ltd in 1915, the new owners did not update the plan after they took over and until mining ceased around 1920.
BATH ROYAL LITERARY & SCIENTIFIC INSTITUTION

This was to prevent young lads and others taking joy rides down the incline when the works were closed, as was to happen on a number of occasions in the future, with considerable damage to the trams and track. When a new rope was ordered in 1928, it was to be 370 yards (338m) long and the same diameter. Ivor Stephens thought that at one time they may have had square wooden trams but remembered the later steel side-tippers. He also recalled a derailment when the rope broke and the descending tram went over. It was due to a pin missing in the rail on the track.

By 1932, according to the map, there was just one longer single self-acting incline with a passing loop halfway down. The incline started at the roadside, where there was the large drum mounted on girders, which replaced an earlier large wheel. Bill Hamlen, the son of Walter, remembers the winding house built in Bath stone and the drum at the top of the incline. It is unknown when the incline was altered; most likely it was after 1921, when all mining had ceased here and the only fuller's earth being processed through the Pan was coming from the Combe Hay mines. As late as during a week in November 1938, it is recorded that the employees, J. Cole, E. Densley and W. Holley, spent a total of 70 hours on slurrying earth brought from Combe Hay and 'letting down' on the incline.

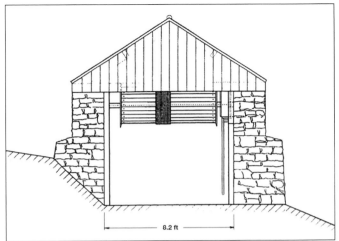

THE PAN GRINDING WORKS

The building in the valley at the bottom of the incline was known as 'The Pan', sometimes called the Middle Works or the Wet Grinding Works. Here, the trams were pushed onto a gantry, one end of the wooden tram was opened and the earth tipped out on the staging and then shovelled into the mortar mill. By the 1930s, there was a turntable at the bottom of the incline leading onto the gantry and the side-tipping tram discharged into shutes that emptied into the actual pan. When the works first opened in 1883, a steam engine drove the rollers, 2 feet (0.6m) in diameter, which revolved in a large rotating cast iron bowl or pan and broke up the clods of earth. The pan itself was 7 feet (2.1m) in diameter and 1.25 feet (0.4m) deep. It was known as an edge-runner and it is possible that it was made by a local firm such as Torrance at Bitton, or Day & English in Bath.

The principle which Dames employed was simple. The fuller's earth was mixed in this mill with about three times as much water being added from the brook, which flows through the valley to Tucking Mill. A dam had been constructed in the early days, to provide a reserve of water for dry periods. Keith Green remembers there was also a small water wheel which, he suggests, probably operated a simple force pump to raise the water some 10 to 15 feet (3-4.6m) from the brook to the height of the mill. A worker named Falconer was dismissed, because he allowed the Pan to go dry and the rollers ground a hole in the bottom!

The early stock return sheets in the days of the Fullers' Earth Union, which were probably the same as those used by the

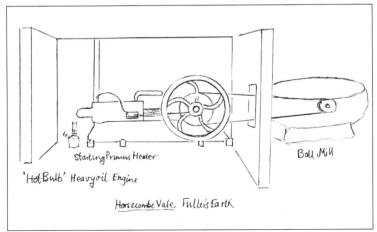

Starting Primus Heater

'Hot Bulb' Heavyoil Engine

Ball Mill

Horsecombe Vale Fuller's Earth

ABOVE LEFT: The Drum was a building in Bath stone adjacent to Midford Road, shown on the 1932 OS map. It would have been very similar to those used at other sites such as the Ochre Mines and Works at Wick, South Gloucestershire.
R.B.J. SMITH & M.J. BREAKSPEAR

ABOVE RIGHT: The Alltwyllt Winding House, used to lower slate down to the Talyllyn Railway in Gwynedd in mid Wales.
DAVID J. MITCHELL, TALYLLYN RAILWAY COMPANY

LEFT: Pan Works. This sketch was made by Keith Green c.1938, showing the main parts of the Pan Grinding Works in Horsecombe Vale.

The mortar mill may have been provided by Day & English, as shown in their advertisement issued in 1885. Joseph Day, inventor of the two-stroke engine, was then operating from his mechanical engineering works at Spring Gardens, just below Pulteney Bridge in Bath. About this time he was also designing a system of high-level waterworks for the neighbourhood.

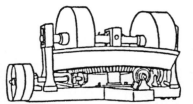

MORTAR MILLS.

These Mills, though perhaps the lowest priced in the market, are thoroughly well-made. The pan revolves and is under driven and rollers working on a turned roller path beneath the pan, relieve the centre bearing from excessive strain.   Great attention has been paid to all wearing surfaces.   Prices include fast and loose pulleys, and the mill is complete as shewn.

Diam. of Pan	Ft. 5	Ft. 6	Ft. 7	Ft 8
Price	£30	£35	£50	£75

Smaller and larger sizes on application.

DAY & ENGLISH,
Engineers & Ironfounders, BATH.

previous owner Garrett (despite changes that had taken place), indicate that steam coal was being used for the engine at the Pan '*for slurrying*', as well as for the steam kilns. They refer to '*mining and letting down to Pan*'. Much later, the forms were changed to read '*Mining and Letting down to Pan (including haulage from Combe Hay).*' By this time, it lists '*Petroleum for Slurrying*' and simply '*Fuel for Drying*'.

Part of Dames process was for the slurry from the mill to be '*turned into a series of little tanks or 'catch-pits', and while the fine fuller's earth remains in a state of suspension, the coarser particles sink to the bottom*'. These catch pits formed a trough some 18 to 20 feet (5.5-6m) in length and 5 feet (1.5m) wide. This was the first stage of sedimentation. At some stage, sand dredgers, with an endless chain of buckets, were used to remove the sand and other unwanted material that had accumulated in the bottom of the catch pits and had to be discarded. The slurry then passed through a sieve before entering the earthenware pipe to Tucking Mill.

When the Fullers' Earth Union took over, improvements were required at the Pan. Extensive repairs were required on the boiler. In May 1917, James Palmer was told by Owen Keevil to erect a Smedley Mortar Mill at the Pan, probably housed in a shed of corrugated iron. Dobson was back in September to supply a mechanical bell to the winding engine house and to build two stone piers at the Pan. It was specified that they were not to be greater than 17 feet apart, because they were to support rails of that length to provide a hoist over the engine cylinder. He was also to insert two

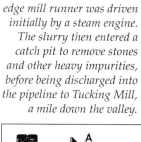

C.R. Dames' Patent. The edge mill runner was driven initially by a steam engine. The slurry then entered a catch pit to remove stones and other heavy impurities, before being discharged into the pipeline to Tucking Mill, a mile down the valley.

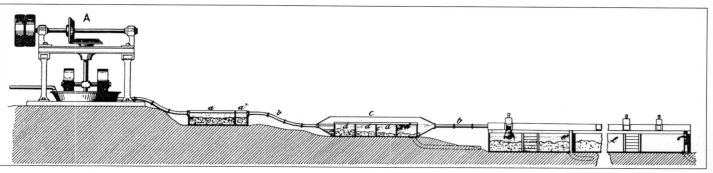

new sieves into the pipeline. In the following January, he was building a new engine house there for £68, probably constructed of Bath stone and with a tiled roof. This may have been the time when steam power was abandoned at the Pan and a Petter two-stroke oil engine, probably using paraffin or kerosene, was installed by November 1918. R.A. Lister did supply such an engine in May 1920 but this may have been for another part of the fuller's earth works. It had a cap on the top of the cylinder which had to be heated with a blow lamp and the exhaust would then keep it going. It was known as a 'hot bulb' engine.

In January 1920, the blacksmith Barrett was asked to repair two ploughs from the mortar mill. The ploughshares inside the pan were probably mounted between the rollers. They would be adjusted to plough up the fuller's earth from the edges and the bottom of the pan, back into the path of the rollers, so that it would be thoroughly ground up and mixed to form the required slurry. A similar arrangement was used in the old olive presses in Greece. Ten more steel ploughshare castings were required for the Pan in 1934.

Further improvements took place in 1928 at the Pan but there are no details. Was this when the

The new boiler, made by Davey Paxman & Co. of Colchester, at the edge of Midford Road prior to being lowered to the engine house at Top Works in 1915. James Palmer is on the left looking at the engine and James Staddon is on the right looking at the camera.
ALEC PALMER

The Davey Paxman Boiler installed in the Engine House at the Top Works, with James Staddon. He lived at Wellow Hill, Combe Hay.
ALEC PALMER

incline was altered and newer trams introduced and, as the 1932 map shows, only one short tramway led from the bottom of the incline to the Pan and the buildings there were altered? In April 1932, there are references to the worn-out chains of the sand dredgers being replaced. Although the exact date is unknown as to when the use of the incline and the Pan finally ceased, the latest date found so far is a weekly return for 6th November 1945, when letting down, slurrying and drying at Tucking Mill all took place. The same reference gives petroleum as being used at the Pan.

Even after the last load of fuller's earth had been let down the incline and all slurrying had stopped at the Pan, the buildings were still maintained for a number of years. Bert Upshall and others were sent over from the Combe Hay Works to paint the shed and Ted Densley broke his arm when he fell off the corrugated roof while tarring it in about 1950! Gilbert Holley remembers helping to dismantle all the plant there and eventually all was demolished by Cliffords, the builders from Southstoke, probably in the 1950s. The plant had been kept in working order although it had not been used for over five years.

THE PIPELINE TO TUCKING MILL

Leaving the Pan Works, the slurry passed through a filter or sieve to remove stones and other unwanted material, before entering an underground pipe of internal diameter 9ins (229mm). The pipe, with inspection manholes, followed the Horsecombe Brook down the valley to the settling tanks at Tucking Mill, a distance of almost a mile, where the second stage of sedimentation took place.

When the pipeline reached the Combe Down Water Works, near the railway viaduct, it was carried in a cast iron pipe on trestles, some of which were quite high, in order to maintain the gradient, and then across the stream on a small bridge. In 1936, the earthenware pipe was broken by vandals and slurrying halted until it was repaired and in 1940 the iron pipe was cracked.

A lot of work had already gone into producing a bag of fuller's earth!

NOTES TO CHAPTER 3

From the **Top Works**, the mine workings extended almost 300 yds (274m) to the west towards the Cross Keys Inn and 290 yds (265m) to the east, 275 yds (251m) to the south west and 308 yds (282m) to the south east.

The building known as '**The Drum**' was recalled by a number of people as being a well-built ashlar structure with three walls, with the drum itself in the open fourth side. When the site was surveyed in May 2003, the foundations were approximately 1.3ft (0.4m) thick, and the building appears to have been 9.8ft (3m) by 9.2ft (2.8m), possibly extended by another 6.6ft (2m) in the direction of the incline. It was probably very similar to the drum house, which dates from c.1895, used at the Ochre Mines and Works at Wick in South Gloucestershire and the Alltwyllt Winding House near Abergynolwyn in Wales, which was used to let slate down to the Tallylyn Railway. The remains of its drum were approximately 10ft (3m) wide and diameter 7.75ft (2.4m) when seen in 2003.

The following dimensions of the **Incline** are as surveyed by Lynn Willies and Neville Redvers-Higgins in May 2003: The incline from the Midford Road to the Top Works as shown on the 1902 map was estimated to be approximately 295ft (90m) long at a slope of 12°. The incline from the Top Works to the bottom of the tramway was approximately 721ft (220m) long, again at a slope of 12°. Thus the overall length of the one tramway, which replaced these two inclines, was 1017ft (310m) and the vertical height the trams descended was approximately 210ft (64m) from Midford Road to the Pan Grinding Works, located a few metres above the Horsecombe Brook. The probable level tramway, which appears to have led to an adit to the east of the main incline, was approximately at the mid-point of the later tramway.

Several people remember the Incline and the Pan in working order during the 1930s. Keith Green made his sketch of the Pan from his visit to it in 1938.

The *Bladud* article called the type of machinery which operated at the **Pan Grinding Works** a 'pug-mill' and clearly states that two heavy rollers rotated round a vat or tank. The noun 'pug' means 'clay which has been ground and mixed with water', while the verb means 'to grind with water and make plastic'. Robertson wrote *'the clod was blunged with water'* and described it as an *'edge-runner mill'* in which the pan was fixed while two vertical crushing rollers, on a single axle, rotated round the pan. The diagram in the Dames' papers shows this kind of mill. Later, this may have been replaced by a mill in which the rollers, rotating on their axle, remained fixed and the pan itself rotated. Both kinds of mill were known as 'mortar mills' or 'pan-mill mixers'. Over the years it is possible that both kinds of mill were used.

The remains of a **water wheel** were found in the brook during the above survey in 2003. Its diameter was 4ft (1.2m), width 1.5ft (0.45m) with twelve spokes. This supports Keith Green's recollection of the water wheel and pump near the Pan which he saw in the 1930s.

Erik August Bolinder was born in Stockholm in 1863 and took over the family firm in 1899. After designing a paraffin engine in 1893, he concentrated on heavy-oil engines and in 1908 produced a very simple two-stoke engine. It had one disadvantage, in that the fuel had to be pre-heated in a vaporiser. Once running, combustion provided enough heat to vaporise the fuel but for starting, a blow-lamp had to be used on the vaporising bulb. It sounds very much like the engine that replaced the 'snorting steam engine' at the Pan.

Miners with dogs and trams. It is believed that this was taken in the Drying Shed at Top Works c.1914. James Staddon is seated on the right, Ernest West is seated between the two dogs and James Coleman is standing next to the trams. The trams have 'blunge' written on their sides, indicating the contents were to be sent down the incline to be slurried at the Pan Works. The frames of the trams were made by Mark Barrett, blacksmith at the Cross Keys Smithy, which closed in 1939.
ALEC PALMER

BIBLIOGRAPHY
Bath Natural History & Antiquarian Field Club Proceedings, Vol. VI, 1889
Bladud, 'The Bath Society Paper', 16th March 1887. Author unknown, possibly H.N. Garrett
Powell, J., 'Fullers Earth from Midford', *BIAS Journal*, Vol. 11, 1978
Smith, R.B.J., & Breakspear, M.J., 'The Ochre Mines and Works at Wick, South Gloucestershire', *BIAS Journal*, Vol. 31, 1998
Willies, Lynn, 'The Midford (Horsecombe Vale) Fuller's Earth Works, Report of a Survey of the Tramway Incline May 2003'. Circulated privately
Woodward, H.B., 'The Jurassic Rocks of Britain', *Memoirs of the Geological Survey of the United Kingdom*, Vol. IV, HMSO 1894

A rare view of the Tucking Mill Works in its original form, possibly c.1887. The chimney has not yet been extended, the tanks are incomplete and the stream is still open. Beyond is the Somerset & Dorset Railway's stone-built Tucking Mill Viaduct before it was widened in 1891/2. This was accomplished simply by encasing the original structure in brick. Just visible on the horizon to the right is the chimney of the De Montalt paper mill. BATH IN TIME, PRIVATE COLLECTION

—≼ **Chapter 4** ≽—

WILLIAM SMITH'S TUCKING MILL
Further Developments 1883-1945

INTRODUCTION

The verdict of a writer at the end of the 19th century on Tucking Mill was '... *a beautiful view is seen all round, somewhat marred, perhaps, by the fuller's earth works, but not altogether.*' Indeed, Stanley Wicks, the son of William Wicks, foreman after the First World War, remembered the works many years later as '*a ramshackle affair which might almost have been flung together in order to catch the Somersetshire Coal Canal which was in decline by this time. There was just a dribble in the canal.*' The buildings had corrugated iron walls and roofs, supported on low brick foundations.

In March 1883, Charles Richard Dames, with his brother George and six other businessmen, had set up a company known as the Midford Fuller's Earth Works Limited, which sought to exploit the deposits from Horsecombe Vale and purify them at new works at Tucking Mill, on the bank of the Somersetshire Coal Canal. They also intended to acquire more property, erect buildings, and '*to construct and maintain any wharves*', indicating that they looked upon the canal as a viable means of transport for their finished products. As late as 1898, a picnic party sailed from Seend in Wiltshire to Dunkerton but by 1906, the canal at Monkton Combe had been drained. These works were built on some 17 acres of land that William Smith (1769-1839) had purchased in 1798 for £1,600 and where one of his tenants, James Sutton, built a water mill in 1808-09 for grinding corn, on the site of an old fulling mill. It was here that Smith and his brother John later set up what proved to be an unsuccessful business for sawing Bath stone about 1811. Tucking Mill was to be a place that Smith loved for the rest of his life and was very sorry to have to leave in 1814 when the business failed.

Charles Richard Dames' Patent No. 2582, 23rd May 1883 'Machinery for the preparation and refining of fuller's earth'. After flowing through the earthenware pipe from the Pan in Horsecombe Vale, the slurry entered the 'The Maggie' at the works at Tucking Mill, 'a long shallow trough where the coarser particles subside, and are caught be a series of small wooden steps placed across the bottom of the trough.'

EARLY PRODUCTION METHODS

The earliest written account we have of the Dames' venture is probably that which appeared in *Bladud*, 'The Bath Society Paper', in March 1887. After describing the processes higher up Horsecombe Vale, it then referred to the slurry leaving the Pan:

'*The pea-soupy looking fluid, containing still a certain amount of extraneous matter, is then allowed to run into a long earthenware drain. When it emerges at the other end it is caught in a long shallow trough called a 'maggie'. As it slowly flows along this trough all the particles of dirt and sand, which keep sinking to the bottom, are caught and detained by a series of little wooden steps placed across the bottom, which rise only a short way up the liquid. It is in fact, a kind of inverted process of skimming, the fuller's earth only requires to have the water dried out of it.*'

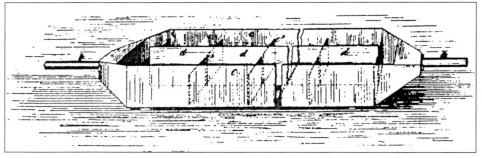

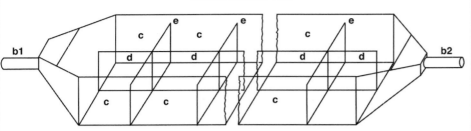

DIAGRAM of A 'MAGGIE' for REMOVING IMPURITIES in FULLER'S EARTH

DAMES PATENT 1883

b1 Slurry from The Pan & first catch pit
b2 Purified slurry to settling tanks
c   Compartments collecting impurities
d   Longitudinal division
e   Baffles or sieves which are hinged at bottom for raising or lowering

The slurry was then led, via a series of channels, into one of the four large tanks where it was allowed to settle. It was claimed that the largest could hold about 1,000 tons! The tanks were about 8-10 feet (2.4-3.0m) deep, one tank was 50-60 feet (15.2-18.8m) long by 30 feet (9m) wide and while one was being filled with slurry, the others would be drained and dug out. Any remaining impurities, being heavier, sank to the bottom first, followed by the almost pure fuller's earth. This settling could take up to thirty days, and during that time, as the water at the top gradually cleared, it was led off by a series of sluice gates. Dames' patent presumably

ABOVE: Diagram of 'The Maggie'. MIKE CHAPMAN

RIGHT: Diagram of the Settling Tanks at Tucking Mill. As the slurry settled, it left clear water above, which could be drained off either by removing the boards in the side of the tank, which were 3-3.5ft wide, 6ins deep and 3ins thick, or by removing the plugs in the 2 inch diameter holes in a vertical drainage pipe or box.
MIKE CHAPMAN

KEY
f. Slurry from the 'Maggie'
g. Sluices to discharge slurry into tank
h. Level of settling slurry
i. Level of clear water above slurry
j. Boards removed to release water as slurry settles
k. Alternative method by removing plugs to release water

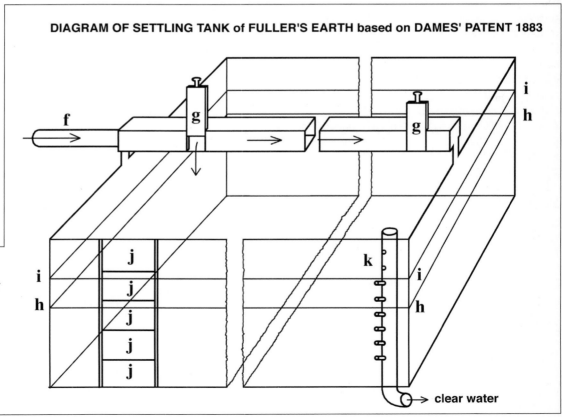

DIAGRAM OF SETTLING TANK of FULLER'S EARTH based on DAMES' PATENT 1883

clear water

included the design of these sluices. The sluice consisted of a series of boards measuring 6ins by 3ins (152mm by 76mm) and between 3 and 3.5 feet (0.9 and 1.1m) wide, which slipped into vertical grooves. Each board contained a perpendicular row of holes, about 2 inches (60mm) in diameter, stopped by wooden pegs, so that when the sediment had sunk below any one of these holes the peg was knocked out and the water allowed to drain off *'in a perfectly pure and drinkable state and very soft.'* A series of these sluices allowed the water level to fall gradually, until there was just damp fuller's earth in the bottom of the tank. Eventually, it reached a consistency where it could be chopped up with a spade. This had to be done with care so as to leave the layer of sand and other impurities undisturbed at the bottom, to be discarded later.

The damp caked earth was then taken along rails in wooden trams, with doors that pulled out at each end, into the kilns where the earth was dried under careful conditions for three to four days. According to the *Bladud* article *'the first step is to put it into an enormous tank, under cover, like a huge swimming bath, 160 feet long, with a floor made of porous tiles. Underneath this floor are nine wide flues, running from a furnace at one end of the drying tank to a tall chimney which stands at some distance from the other end. When a roaring fire is kept up in the furnace, which is fifteen feet in width and eight in depth and has three fire-doors, a tremendous draught is created between the fire and the chimney.'* The top of the chimney was some 300 feet from the furnace and apart from the buildings.

The result of this draught was that it drew the moisture out of the earth into the flues. It was described as *'looking like a great cauldron of boiling mud, the surface heaving and quivering, and covered with bubbles. The door of this chamber is within a few feet of the Canal bank, so that when the drying is accomplished the stuff is simply put into sacks and trundled on board the barges which are ready to receive it. Then by land and sea, it makes its way all over the world.'* These were the *'improvements in the Method of and Machinery or Appliances for the Preparation and Refining of Fuller's Earth'* according to the Letters Patent submitted by Dames in May 1883.

Then in 1884, when production had reached 864 tons for the year, *'One of the great tanks, just filled with slurry, gave way at the side, the deluge which followed doing a considerable amount of damage to the recently erected works.'* The resulting damage to the works cost around £500 and this was probably the reason why the Dames' leased the works to H.N. Garrett in 1885. Dames' business was finally wound up in July 1887, when it appears Garrett became the manager of a new company known as The Midford Fuller's Earth Refining Works on the same site. He was there on 26th February 1889, when the Bath Field Club erected the memorial tablet to William Smith, the father of English geology, on the building next to the cottage *'by kind permission of Mr. Garrett, the proprietor of the Fuller's Earth Works adjoining.'*. In 1890, George Dames sold the leasehold of the beds of fuller's earth to the Fullers' Earth Union which had been formed in that year and of which he was secretary for a few years. Garrett appears to have put Walter Allen Sheppard, a local quarrymaster, in charge as manager in 1890. Five years later Garrett bought the processing rights from C.R. Dames.

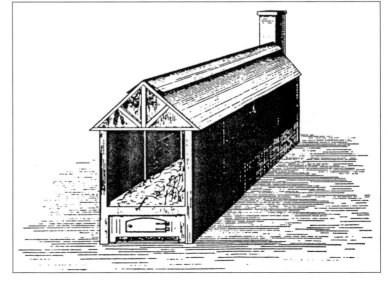

The Drying Shed, from the Patent. The kiln had metal plates or tiles. Midford Fuller's Earth Works Ltd.

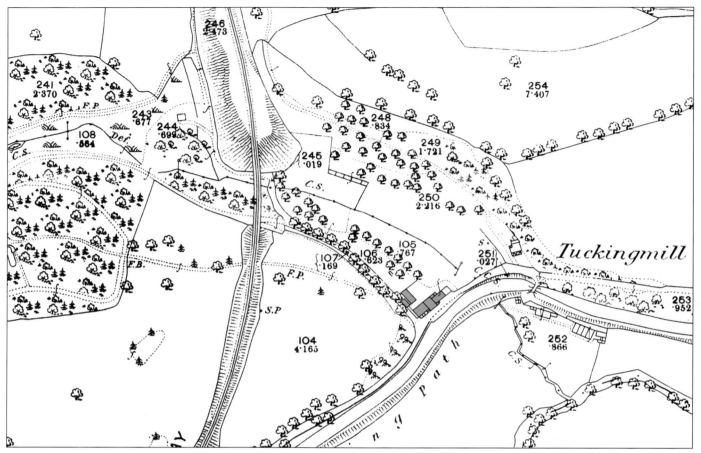

1884 25in OS showing Tucking Mill, with the Somerset & Dorset Railway crossing over the viaduct, centre left, and the Somersetshire Coal Canal occupying the bottom right corner of the map.

DEVELOPMENTS UNDER H.N. GARRETT

In June 1901, Midford Castle, which owned the works at Tucking Mill, the Top Works and the Pan Grinding Works, together with various plots of land, was put up for sale by auction. The notice of sale stated:

> 'the right to dig fuller's earth. The whole of this Lot is sold subject to the lease to Mr H.N. Garrett. Fuller's earth is obtained from the upper slopes of the hill and taken to a mill where it is roughly mixed and thence it goes in liquid condition through pipes to Tucking Mill where its preparation is completed. The corrugated iron buildings both here and at the Upper Mill have been put up by the lessee and are removable by him.'

In the end, the fuller's earth works were not offered for sale because the reserve price was not reached. The Trustees of Midford Castle eventually sold the land at Tucking Mill and Horsecombe Vale to Garrett at the end of 1905, even though the lease had another twenty-four years to run. The schedule for an earlier unsuccessful sale stated that the buildings at Tucking Mill included a six-

Tucking Mill Cottage and Mill, c.1889. This shows the buildings before H.N. Garrett started to develop the site, by introducing the milling of some of the fuller's earth in the building to the right of the cottage. Note the wharf on the opposite side of the road is clear of rushes.
DR NORMAN,
BATH REFERENCE LIBRARY

roomed cottage used as offices and stores, an old building used as a store, a forge and a small stable.

Henry Newson Garrett had a chequered history. He was born at Leiston in Suffolk in July 1841, one of the sons of Richard Garrett of the engineering works in that town. When Richard died in 1866, his three sons inherited the works but Henry was thrown out of the business in 1878. He moved to Bath that year and bought a large house at 101 Sydney Place, where he was to live until his death in October 1912. This was also the business address for his ventures in the fuller's earth industry, both at Wellow and at Midford. The mining at Wellow appears to have ended in January 1894, after which he devoted all his energies to Midford, where his son Alec Henry Garrett was manager for a time until his death in the spring of 1907. Six months after Garrett's own death, a new company known as H.N. Garrett (Bath) Ltd. was formed on 22nd March 1913, possibly in preparation to selling out to the Fullers' Earth Union.

During the years that Garrett ran the business there were undoubtedly changes and improvements to the methods of preparation. It seems that Garrett arranged for the fuller's earth first to be partially dried on steam kilns and then transferred to the fire kilns to be finished off. The earth from the drying shed was almost pure and was referred to as 'washed and refined lump'. It may be that, for some customers, the first drying was sufficient as regards to moisture content and that some of this product was then milled, as it was claimed that ground fuller's earth never came into contact with the fumes from the solid fuel fires. In the fire kiln, the earth was spread out on perforated iron plates under which the hot flue gases were passing. The plates were supported on piers made of brick or railway sleepers some 1 to 1.5 feet (0.3-0.45m) high and the flues were brick lined. The drying process

ABOVE: The Cornish Boiler. This 12ft long boiler supplied the steam for the steam kiln and the water pump which filled the boiler. It was located parallel to the brook on the east side of the buildings and opposite the furnace for the fire kiln. ROGER CROKER

ABOVE RIGHT: The Furnace. This supplied the hot gases which passed under the floor of the kiln causing the earth 'to bubble like hot porridge'. It was located in the stoke hole opposite the Cornish boiler. The fire kiln was on a higher level than the steam kiln. JOHN POWELL

required great care because if the earth was burnt in any way it was useless. It was the responsibility of the stoker to turn the earth regularly, breaking up the clods, to prevent this happening and to this end a night stoker was employed. For some customers, the state of the earth was now sufficient for their needs and it was bagged up either as granules or small lumps the size of walnuts and sold as 'Lump fuller's earth'.

Garrett's smooth plates at Tucking Mill prevented contamination of the earth, as he was keen to supply the purest and finest fuller's earth powder possible for certain customers, such as those in the oil refining and pharmaceutical industries. To this end, he must have introduced a milling process using some of the dried earth. This was carried out in the old mill adjoining Tucking Mill cottage, using two grindstones which may have been left from the early days of 19th century flour milling. The grindstones were situated at the bottom of the building at ground level, behind a flap that is visible in some photographs. After Garrett's time, it was commented that he did not have much in the way of elevators and it may be that earth for milling was brought round to the front of the building and hoisted up to the gantry which he had installed there.

Robertson has commented that milled fuller's earth was not necessary for the woollen industry but the oil industry required a refined powder form of the earth. When Dames had set up the works at Tucking Mill, he was aiming at the textile industry, whereas Garrett tried to get into the United States' oil refining market and hence it is most likely that it was he who started milling at the works. The discovery in the 1880s that fuller's earth could be used to discolour glyceride oils led to a growing demand for the product. Robertson has pointed out that in fact Tucking Mill produced the best fuller's earth for fulling, because the grit had been removed from it. In the early days at Tucking Mill, Garrett did produce bleached earth but there are no details as to how this was made.

Another improvement carried out by Garrett was the purchase in 1895 of a Babcock steam engine.

This powered the winding gear, which winched a flatbed trolley on rails up the gradient from the loading bay to the road for transferring onto carts. The trolley carried 2 cwt (100kg) sacks of fuller's earth. The $^3/_4$ inch (19mm) stranded steel hawser was blocked off with trestles or planks to prevent anyone falling over it when it was in use! A new goods siding to the north of Midford railway station was built specially to load the fuller's earth. A carter named Bill Seal, employed by Garrett, took the sacks of earth from the works up to the siding until the First World War.

POSSIBLE DEVELOPMENT OF THE BUILDINGS AT TUCKING MILL

At this distance in time, it is not easy to chart the development of the use of the mill and the buildings beside the lane. The following is put forward as a result of examining maps and photographs, the recorded memories of some who lived at Tucking Mill early in the 20th century, and the research of others. The mill buildings may not have been used in the days of Dames but Garrett needed to mill some of the earth to make it suitable not only for cloth factories but also soap and cosmetic manufacturers and the oil industry. On his notepaper in 1896, Garrett described himself as a trader in '*refined and concentrated fuller's earth*' but by 1907, he changed this to a '*Fuller's Earth Refiner and Rectifier*' and the product was the well known 'Washed and Refined'.

By 1904, what appears to be a covered way extended along the back of these buildings, possibly over a tramway and turntable that brought the dried earth from the kilns, either to be milled or stored in the building next to the mill. There was also a new tall extension at the back of the old mill. Did this contain a boiler and steam engine to power the elevator and the mill? A metal flue beside the mill chimney is clearly visible in some photographs and in the sketch showing the barge *Rose* moored at the nearby wharf in the late 1890s. The sketch by Louie Wheatcroft appeared in June 1898 in *The Bath & County Graphic*. The entrance to the mill was said to be at the rear of the building and there was also an office here. Later, there was an old boiler outside the Babcock House, in which the

ABOVE LEFT: The Chimney. It was demolished by J. Dawson & Sons on 13th February 1968 for the sum of £65. The chimney was of square section, approximately 80ft high, having been extended at some date from 70ft. It was last used in 1946. BATH CHRONICLE

ABOVE: Under the Kilns. The steel-plated floor has been removed, during the demolition of the works in 1978, to reveal the channels along which the hot gases from the furnace would have passed to dry the earth. JOHN POWELL

RIGHT: Tucking Mill Fuller's Earth Works. A sketch by the local artist Mrs. Louie Wheatcroft showing the canal still in water with the barge Rose *alongside the wharf. 'A beautiful view is seen all round, somewhat marred, perhaps by the Fuller's Earth Works, but not altogether.' THE BATH & COUNTY GRAPHIC NEW SERIES III.2, JUNE 1898*

BELOW: 1902 25in OS, showing the further development of the works.

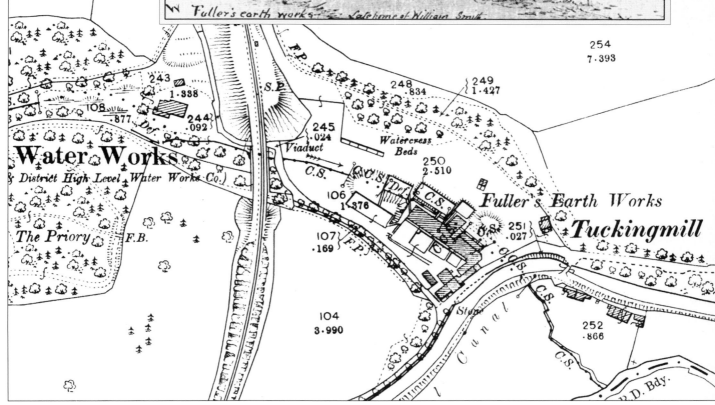

Tucking Mill Cottage and Mill, c.1902-04. The corrugated shed for the Babcock engine has been added at the far end, possibly for the steam winch, whilst the mill building has acquired a gantry and hoist. To the rear, there is a completed new building which may have housed a system of buckets and chain to lift the dried fuller's earth to the top of the building for milling. The centre building may have been where the fuller's earth was stored, prior to being despatched through the doorway (window) above the level of the cart which is drawn alongside. There appears to be a new structure on the roof of this building. Note the canal appears to be low in water.
DR WALMSLEY

Wicks' children used to play. This may have been taken out when it was no longer in use, because a road had been put in which enabled Hamlen's lorry to get in closer for loading, so removing the need for the winch and cable required in the days of horses and carts.

The building next to the mill could well have been the main storage area both for 'lump' and 'milled' earth. It had a doorway at a convenient height for loading road vehicles. A dray appears in some photographs standing alongside. Next came the fitting shop and workshop where, for example, an old man named Nathan Chappell mended the hessian sacks. There had to be somewhere to carry out essential repairs and maintenance. Finally a new building at the end, constructed of corrugated iron, was probably the 'Babcock House'. A small pipe or vent through the roof, possibly for exhaust

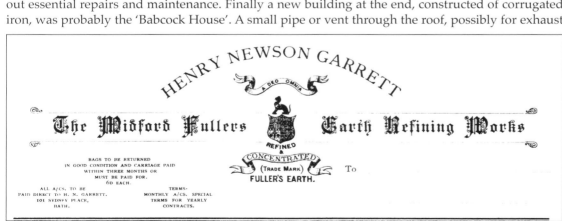

H.N. Garrett's headed notepaper. Garrett succeeded the Dames' brothers at Tucking Mill and remained in business there from 1887 until his death in 1912. By 1907, he was calling himself 'Refiner and Rectifier'.
FULLER'S EARTH ARCHIVES, MUSEUM OF BATH AT WORK

MIDFORD. FULLERS EARTH WORKS

A slightly later view of Tucking Mill Cottage and Mill, probably c.1905-06. The canal is partly drained.
ALEC PALMER

steam, appears in some photographs.

Garrett clearly enlarged the works; possibly he added extra settling tanks and built the gantry and hoist on the front of the old mill. This may have been used by him before installing a chain hoist, a vertical continuous chain with cups, or it could have been kept for use when the latter was being repaired or if there was only a small amount to mill. In that case, the dry earth would be brought round from the kilns to the front of the building and hoisted to the top floor. The fuller's earth was taken up to a hopper at the top of a rickety staircase behind the hoist doors. Vera Morris, who, as a child, lived in the cottage for some twelve years from 1914, recalled how the whole house shook when the mill was running. This usually occurred about once a week or month according to demand, and all the windows and doors had to be closed because of the dust. The resulting very fine powder produced a great deal of dust and had the consistency of talcum powder. They used it for baby powder! Sacks were then filled and put into waiting carts or, when the canal was still in operation, carried across to a barge.

Stan Wicks described his recollections of the works in the 1920s as follows:

'Walking along the lane from Midford, Tucking Mill Cottage was on the left with the mill adjoining it. An ash driveway then turned down into the works and the loading bay. Behind this bay there was a primitive changing room where the men could dry their clothes and wipe their wooden clogs with

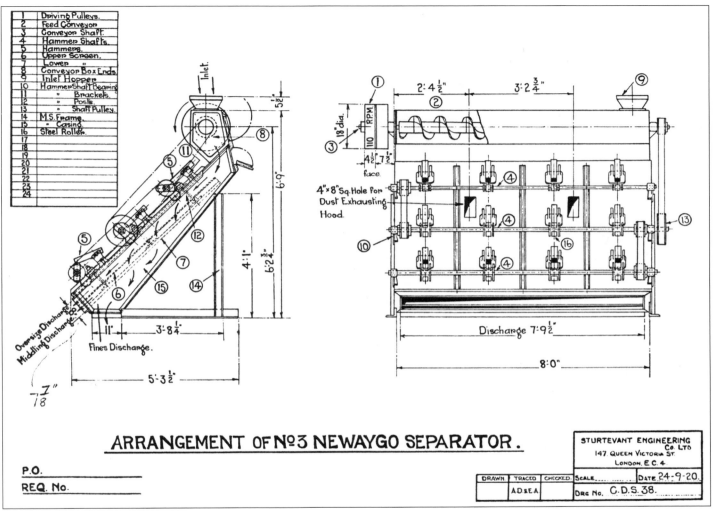

1	Driving Pulleys.
2	Feed Conveyor
3	Conveyor Shaft.
4	Hammer Shafts.
5	Hammers.
6	Upper Screen.
7	Lower "
8	Conveyor Box Ends.
9	Inlet Hopper
10	Hammer Shaft Bearing
11	" Brackets.
12	" Posts.
13	" Shaft Pulley.
14	M.S. Frame.
15	" Casing.
16	Steel Roller.
17	
18	
19	
20	
21	
22	
23	
24	

ARRANGEMENT OF Nº 3 NEWAYGO SEPARATOR.

P.O.
REQ. No.

STURTEVANT ENGINEERING Co. Ltd
147. Queen Victoria St.
London. E.C. 4

DRAWN.	TRACED	CHECKED.	SCALE.	DATE 24-9-20.
	A.D.&E.A.		DRG No. C.D.S. 38.	

greasy oil. The hot plates in the kilns would have burnt shoes or boots, and hob-nailed boots were not allowed in case they contaminated the earth. Their lower legs were protected with sacking spats. A culvert, carrying the gurgling Horsecombe Brook on its way to join the Midford Brook, ran under the ash driveway and some of the buildings.'

Entering the buildings, the 12 feet (3.7m) long Cornish boiler, stoke hole and, on a slightly lower level, the furnace with its three fire doors were on the left, and behind this and further to the left was the fire kiln. Further back was the steam kiln, with the tramways that led outside to the tanks on the right and further up the site. The steam pipes were lagged between the buildings but not under the steam kiln plates. A steam-driven donkey engine pumped water into the boiler. There was a box for the stoker to sit on and a piece of sacking hung between the Cornish boiler and the steam engine.

The Newago Separator. This machine was installed at Tucking Mill c.1920 as a preliminary sifter. When milling ceased there, it was taken to the works on Odd Down. Its purpose was to produce various mesh sizes of fuller's earth powder as required by different customers.
FULLER'S EARTH ARCHIVES, MUSEUM OF BATH AT WORK

View from the Somerset & Dorset Joint Railway's Tucking Mill Viaduct c.1906. The ramshackle nature of the buildings, made of corrugated iron, can be seen. In the foreground is the 'Big Tank', one of the large settling tanks into which the slurry, piped down the valley from the Pan Works, was discharged. Another tank appears to have footprints across the fuller's earth which has settled in the bottom of it. The later extension to the chimney is clearly visible. William Smith's house is to the left of the works.
ALEC PALMER

Stan remembered when he was sent inside the Cornish boiler to chip off the lime, the work being lit by a candle stuck in a lump of fuller's earth. He was about seven at the time and the job took two days, with his father's help, and he received 2s 6d (12.5p) for his labours. The chimney, some 300 feet (90m) from the furnace, and the biggest tank were beyond the buildings on the left. A large barrow was used to collect the coal and to carry the ash from the furnace to be dumped in large heaps near the bottom of the garden of Tucking Mill House, the true home of William Smith. Much of this ash would be used later to fill the canal.

Around the site there were the settling tanks of different size and construction. The 'Big Tank', near the chimney, was constructed from baulks of timber covered on the outside with packed earth and about 9 feet (2.75m) deep. The small tank, constructed in the same way, was very shallow and seldom used. The 'New Tank' was of concrete and 5 feet (1.5m) deep. It seems that the three tanks on the west side of the kilns were deep and of brick, rendered with sand and cement. There was also a rarely used smaller tank only 2 feet (0.6m) deep. The number of tanks was less in later years, reducing from the seven before 1904 to five at the end. It may be that some tanks on the north and east were not repaired. A brick-lined water tank, which measured 60 feet by 55 feet (18m by 17m), was built in 1918 to provide a reservoir for the boilers.

By the outbreak of the First World War, there were three drying sheds with the steel plated floors and one with a wooden floor. A set of rails was laid from the big and new tanks to what was called the 'steam kiln'. Wet earth was transferred, using small trucks, from the tanks to this drying area and then, when partially dried, to the 'fire kiln' to complete the process. The product, in walnut sized lumps, was then shovelled onto a large iron plate that spanned the six foot deep culvert. Close by the fire kiln, the sacks were filled on a pair of scales with 2 cwt (100kg) of fuller's earth. The sacks were sewn up with string and were ready for despatch. This loading area was the scene of an accident one night in April 1930 when the stoker, Arthur Gerrish, was buried under several tons of earth he was piling onto the plate. The iron plate had given way and he was taken to hospital for treatment to his injuries. Arthur Gerrish, who was related to 'Smacker' Gerrish, the driver of the steam waggon, lived at Tucking Mill Cottage in the 1920s, after the Morris family.

When the Fullers' Earth Union took over, they employed William Hamlen, who ran a coal merchant's business at Midford goods yard, to transport the earth. When a load was ready, Stan Wicks remembers being sent with a note to Mr Hamlen,

Tucking Mill Cottage and Mill, c.1908-14. Changes from the previous photograph of the works include a door in the central building having been blocked up and shutters added. Note the canal is now dry.
ALEC PALMER

who then came with his wagon and three or four horses. As the floor of the works, the trolley and the dray were all at the same height, the heavy sacks could be moved without too much difficulty. Hamlens would deliver a two-ton load to the goods yard at Midford and bring back coal for the furnaces. The method employed by the carters was to get up a good speed with the horses in order to climb the hill to the sidings. Sometimes, the Wicks' and Morris' children rode on the cart back to the works. The Fullers' Earth Union's own steam waggon was used from 1916 to transport fuller's earth to the various railway yards and also to Combe Hay Works. When milling ceased at Tucking Mill in the 1920s, the steam waggon would take earth to be milled there.

FURTHER DEVELOPMENTS

The Fullers' Earth Union acquired Garrett's business in July 1915 and, in a report written by Owen Keevil that September, he pointed out that at Tucking Mill, the mill was in a very run down state, the tanks needed repairs and the power plant would have to be replaced. There would have to be a major renovation of the works. He thought that Garrett may have got into financial difficulties and become bankrupt by not charging a remunerative rate for his 'Washed and Refined' lump earth.

It was arranged to purchase a secondhand boiler for Tucking Mill Works, as this was required to enable drying of the fuller's earth to be resumed. This boiler was originally made in 1884 by Garrett's of Leiston in Suffolk and is referred to as a *'Cornish multi-tubular boiler'* in the insurance inspection. Thus it was not until the early part of 1916 that production could start properly, after the boiler had been installed. By March, the new mill was expected to be working but no longer using stones to grind the earth. When Owen Keevil took over, it was his intention to produce '90 mesh' powder at Tucking Mill.

In July 1917, Dobson was called in to erect a new 'lump' elevator and a new chute from the dresser (a screen or sieving device) to the bin. Despite these improvements, the old mill buildings

Plan of the Fuller's Earth Works at Tucking Mill. This plan has been compiled from the various OS maps of the site, a sketch plan prepared from memory by Alec Palmer c.1981, and with assistance from Roger and Ian Croker. The exact nature of all the buildings is unknown, and the kilns and tramways are approximate. The flues to the chimney ran along the south side of the sheds. The kiln floors were steel-plated, while the extension to the east had a wooden floor. The stream was partly in a culvert. The trolley was pulled up the ash track by a cable, the winch probably being in the 'Babcock House'.
ALEC PALMER

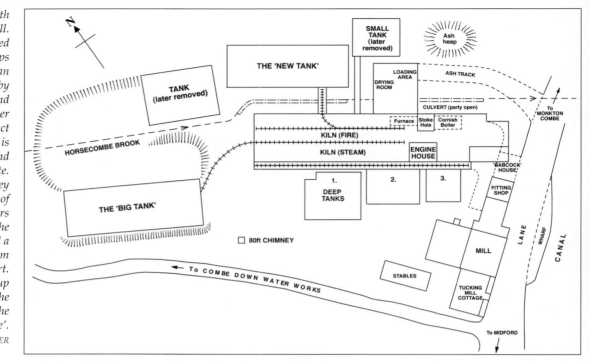

at Tucking Mill became increasingly dilapidated, the floors were rotting, the roof leaked and in 1918 Keevil doubted that this building would ever be used again. Does this suggest it was the front of the building, being the old mill, that was in a bad state and that the actual milling now took place in a new structure at the rear? By August 1919, when the main grinding plant at Combe Hay Works had been shut down for two months in order to install a more powerful plant, the company 'had been kept going with a smaller plant at the other Works [Tucking Mill] and that this had now given out.'

What powered the mill? A metal flue beside the mill chimney, which is visible in some photographs, and in the sketch of Tucking Mill is shown smoking, suggests that the mill did in fact have its own engine. This seems to be confirmed, because in January 1919 the company 'wanted to restore the drain from Tucking Mill Cottage to the old culvert which was rendered useless some years ago when cut in two by the sinking of the Engine Flywheel Pit.'

In January 1919, there was trouble getting washed and refined earth 'because of ice [mixed] with earth from the tanks', when normally at least 15 tons per week were being dried at the works. Another problem was in attracting enough staff. Writing in January 1918 to his father in Redhill, Keevil said 'if you want more washed and refined earth during the period of the War it can be got and I must take on the necessary labour, but I must tell you frankly that if this is to be done expense must be no object. To get men to work in the tanks at Tucking Mill and to get them to leave more congenial jobs, and put up with the filthy mess and the wet and the cold feet and legs inseparable from this job, I must offer fancy wages and outbid everyone in this neighbourhood who has more congenial jobs to offer.' Relatives of one of the men who worked there said that it was a dreadful job getting into the tanks and digging out the putty-like slurry and moving it to the kilns. The Fullers' Earth Union paid 2d less than almost any other firm in Bath in April 1920. The men worked a

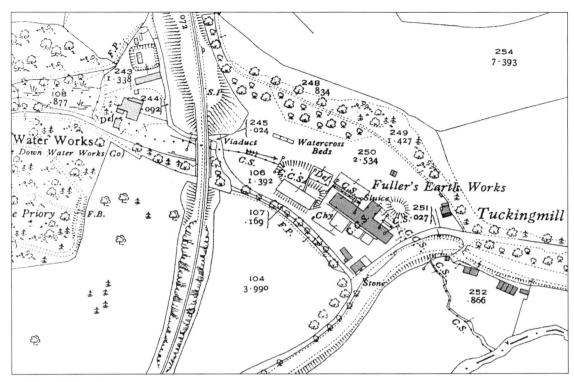

1930 25in OS of Tucking Mill, after demolition of the buildings facing the road.

48-hour week for £3 10s (£3.50) and an annual bonus of £6, in lieu of a week's paid leave.

W.F. Keevil arranged for his son to send him the Midford mill shaft and rollers in September 1919, to make them more durable and reliable. He also advised Owen to prepare about 100 tons of '140 mesh' powder every year at Midford. By October, Wicks, who had now replaced Palmer as foreman, reported that the steam kilns were unusable and there was trouble with the fire kiln. In February 1920, 16 tons were being produced each week but this gradually declined, due in part to the depression that affected the Yorkshire woollen mills. The No. 1 slurry tank needed repair in June, both the floor and the brickwork required rendering, and Dobson patched up the floor with cement. Owen Keevil had reported to his father that all three tanks were in a deplorable condition. He thought that they needed to be rebuilt. He pointed out the next month that a sand and cement grout was not satisfactory, as it got into the fuller's earth and so made the product useless.

The debate over the whole process at Tucking Mill continued. W.F. Keevil spoke of the trade in washed and refined earth being transferred to Combe Hay, '*the slurrying of fuller's earth is obsolete, unnecessary and indefensible*' from a business point of view; '*We took the tanks over in an altogether unsatisfactory state*' and they had either to be put right or they would have to '*quit selling washed and refined as refined stuff, free from all dangerous matter.*' Even though some of the managers of the Fullers' Earth Union thought that the whole process of slurrying was obsolete, it was to be carried on for another twenty years until the mid-1940s, using earth brought from Combe Hay! Its main virtue was that it had been sold as 'Washed and Refined' from the earliest days at Tucking Mill and there was still a demand for this product, especially from some customers in the woollen trade in Yorkshire.

*The Cross Keys Smithy.
Mark Barrett, the
blacksmith, carried out a lot
of work here for the fuller's
earth works, until he closed
in 1939.*
ROGER CLIFFORD COLLECTION

W.F. Keevil was all in favour of the customers just having 'crude blue lump', pointing out that the milled earth was *'very dusty'*.

During the early 1920s, it is unlikely that any milling took place, as Stan Wicks could remember the chain hoist, used to carry the lump up to a hopper at the top of the building, being unused and covered with dust. For a while, these works had really only been maintained to help out those at Combe Hay in times of high demand or when the plant there was being repaired. Henceforth, any customer who specified the washed and refined milled product, would receive fuller's earth that had been through the slurrying process at the Pan and Tucking Mill and then taken back to Combe Hay Works to be milled. 'Everite' asbestos roofing, supported on a timber frame, was installed in 1924 to replace the corrugated iron sheets on the sheds. The buildings were described as being crude, having walls of corrugated asbestos or thin slabs of Bath stone mounted on a low brick base, the bricks having come from the Cattybrook brickworks at Shortwood, near Bristol.

In 1926, the decision was taken to demolish all the buildings that faced the road. They had become dangerous to passers-by and were pulled down the next year. This involved moving the plaque recognising William Smith to the adjacent cottage, built in 1808 by one of his tenants. This has caused the confusion that still exists as to where Smith lived. He actually lived nearby, in what is now the

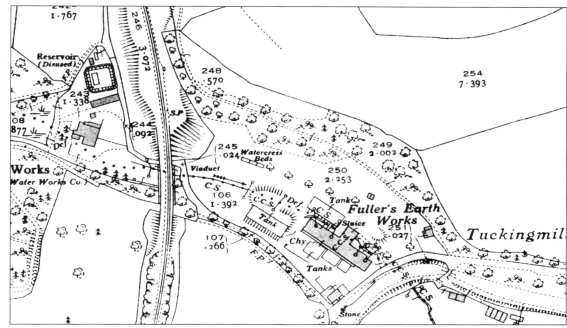

1939 25in OS of Tucking Mill, the last mapping before the works closed.

western part of Tucking Mill House. According to Pitcairn & Richardson's guide to the area, the cottage was the office of the fuller's earth factory in 1924. This may have been only a room and for a short time but it could account for the fact that for some years the postal address of the industry was 'Combe Hay Works, Midford'. Vera Morris also thought that there was an office in part of the cottage or mill buildings. A telephone may have been installed around 1916, so that there could be contact with Redhill and the Combe Hay Works.

After all the hard work to produce this refined fuller's earth for the market, there were often complaints from customers. Some found it coarse and sandy. Even though large amounts of sand and grit were removed at the Pan, some still found its way into the final washed and refined product. Most of it would be deposited at the bottom of the tanks at Tucking Mill but some of the fuller's earth would inevitably contain unwanted material. Other customers complained about the moisture content being too high. It was a problem to achieve the right level of moisture in the finished product but there was the added risk of it becoming damp when the order was despatched by rail or sea.

THE LAST DAYS OF PRODUCTION

During the Second World War, production at Tucking Mill virtually ceased, with the steam kilns last being used about 1940 and the fire kilns around 1945. For a time, the plant was used to dry raw earth that had been brought from the workings at Combe Hay. In 1942, a 6-ton load of the mixture known as SP4 was dried at Tucking Mill and then taken back to Combe Hay Works for grinding. Further loads followed when there was a demand but soon after the war, the plant was being used only to store bagged fuller's earth powder from Combe Hay. According to the records of the steeplejacks Dawson & Sons, the chimney was last used in 1946. They recorded that it was square in section and approximately 80 feet (24m) high, and that it had been heightened by 10 feet (3m) at some later

William Smith's house at Tucking Mill c.1918. The nearer part of the house is the original. James Palmer stands in front, with three of his children, Albert, Pearl and Ruby. Notice the roof-line of William Smith's house compared with today.
ALEC PALMER

date. They were responsible for its demolition on 13th February 1968 at a cost of £65.

After the Second World War, activated fuller's earth (SDC and SQC), produced at Redhill, was stored in the sheds at Tucking Mill after production had ceased there. Ed Croker remembered articulated lorries coming from Redhill with 20 tons of activated earth, which were stored temporarily and then taken by rail to Llandarcy oil refinery near Neath in South Wales. The sheds could store up to 500 tons. This resulted in a busy period for the old works at Tucking Mill in September 1948, when 160 tons of stored earth were despatched. Holmes, the manager in Bath, was to write '*it is a long time since Midford was so busy*.' The following year, 10,000 bags of prepared fuller's earth products were in store.

THE STAFF

James Palmer is thought to have spent a considerable time at Tucking Mill in 1893, before moving there permanently when the mining at Wellow ceased the following year. About that time, he commented on the state of the nearby Somersetshire Coal Canal which still had some water '*what a shame to lose the water. It will become a wilderness.*' In a letter dated 30th July 1896, H.N. Garrett acknowledged Palmer's help: '*You have done your best I know for me thro' bad times and I hope we shall have better times presently.*' This could be referring to a decline in trade or difficulties with the plant at Tucking Mill but it seems clear that the two men got on well together, as Palmer was to remain with him to the very end of Garrett's company.

James Palmer worked in the industry for some twenty-five years, first at Wellow and then at Tucking Mill, where he was the foreman for a number of years living in William Smith's house with his large family. There were difficulties with the new management when the Fullers' Earth Union took over in 1915. Palmer, who had been a supervisor, found himself on '*messy tank work*' under Owen Keevil and his wages were reduced. It seems that the two men did not get on and the former was accused of falsifying his stock returns of washed and refined fuller's earth in July 1919, with the result that customers did not receive their orders on time. This may have been the final straw and Palmer and his family left Tucking Mill House and the company. Palmer also claimed that the men were being ordered to mix sand in with the refined fuller's earth and he had not agreed with this policy. Robertson has suggested that this may have been ordered as the demand for the fine earth, once used by the pharmaceutical industry, had declined and that less pure earth was acceptable for laying the coal dust in mine galleries. Coal dust was known to have caused explosions in the North Somerset mines in the past. He added that the management should have explained to the men why they were mixing in the impurities.

During a greater part of its life, the whole Tucking Mill enterprise was staffed by very few men, resulting in long hours of heavy work often in harsh conditions. This was acknowledged by Keevil, who realised that it would always be difficult to attract workers and retain them. During the First World War, both day and night working was resumed, it being necessary to have a man on duty to tend the fires for the kilns. The staff had to be prepared to work at the Horsecombe mines, the Top Works, the Pan and Tucking Mill, as well as Combe Hay. This involved long walks between the various sites. Men were transferred between the sites if, for example, the workings at Combe Hay were flooded or if Tucking Mill was cut off by snowdrifts. Staff were quickly dismissed if orders declined. Wicks, who had come to work at Tucking Mill about 1909 and become foreman after Palmer, was dismissed in 1924 after reprimanding a stoker for allowing the earth to burn on the fire kiln.

POSTSCRIPT

In 1940, Tucking Mill Cottage was requisitioned for evacuees from London and later used to accommodate families from Bath, who had been bombed out in the air raids of April 1942. It was finally sold by the Company in 1963 for £818.

The Wessex Water Authority, known today as Wessex Water plc, acquired the fuller's earth works in 1978 and demolished all the buildings used for drying and the settling tanks. The company redeveloped the site the next year, excavating a storage reservoir for water pumped from the River Avon. The story of Tucking Mill had almost come full circle, as the 1840 Tithe map shows that a large pond occupied much the same site. William Smith would have rejoiced to see that the place he loved so much had been restored to its original beauty and tranquillity.

NOTES TO CHAPTER 4

In 1794, the **Somersetshire Coal Canal** was authorised by '*An Act for making and maintaining a Navigable Canal with certain Rail Ways, and Stone Roads, from several Collieries … and the making of Rail or Carriage Ways, or Stone Roads, for the Passage of Waggons and other Carriages to and from such Canal, will open a Communication … in the said Counties of Somerset and Wilts, whereby the Carriage and Conveyance of Coal, Lime, and Stone, Marl, Fuller's Earth … will be greatly facilitated and rendered less expensive than at present …*'

Evidence that the ruins of the **original tucking mill** existed in William Smith's day are suggested by his short poem headed '*Vales of Bath, Tucking Mill, Doncaster 1825*':

'*As wild as were the woods of Bath*
When Bladud trod their thorny path
And bathed his Hogs
In steaming Bogs
Just o'er the hill was Tucking Mill
In scrambling through that thorny ground
Amidst the waste
The site I found
The old foundations traced.'

*Tablet to William Smith. Inscription: '*Here lived WILLIAM SMITH, Father of English Geology, Born 23rd March, 1769, Died 28th August 1839*'. This tablet was originally erected on the mill buildings by the Bath Field Club on 26th February 1889 '*by kind permission of Mr Garrett, the proprietor of the fuller's earth works adjoining*'. The mill buildings were demolished in 1927 and the tablet re-erected in 1932, by the Geological Society of London and the Bath Royal Literary & Scientific Institute, on Tucking Mill Cottage (shown here), not on his house. This has caused the confusion as to where William Smith actually lived.*
MIKE CHAPMAN

Another poem by William Smith which shows his love for the area:

'I made the axeman's axe resound,
the oaks were levelled to the ground.
The thorn and briar crack'd on fire.
The goodly ground was cleared
and fruits and garden shrubs appeared.
Great plans were laid, a fish pond made
combining taste with trade.
That wandering path which leads to Bath
contrived to ease the hill
and Freestone Blocks torn from the rocks
run down to yonder mill.
O Tucking Mill I love thee still
and oft afar in fancy trace
my musings there beneath thy bower.
'Tis contemplation's place.'

The 1901 Notice of **Sale of Midford Castle**:

'Lot 2. The Midford Fullers' Earth Works, comprising the Tucking Mill now used for the preparation of Fullers' Earth for the Market, situate adjoining the road from Midford to Monkton Combe, also a Cottage and Garden with various Closes of Land …

The right to dig the Fullers' Earth [in Horsecombe Vale] *is included in this Lot, and the Royalty reserved by the Lease for Fullers' Earth under such Lands also is included. The whole of this Lot is sold subject to the Lease to Mr H.N. Garrett, but with the benefit of Rents and Royalties thereby reserved, which lease has 24¹/₄ years to run.*

The Corrugated Iron Buildings both here [Tucking Mill] *and at the Upper Mill* [Top Works] *have been put up by the Lessee, and are removable by him.*

There is a wayleave of 2d. per ton for all Fullers' Earth obtained under land not belonging to the Vendors conveyed over this Lot or through the pipes [pipeline from the Pan] mentioned above. This wayleave is included in the Sale.'

Robertson's papers contain a critique of Powell's article in the *BIAS Journal*, Vol. 11, in which he corrects a number of points.

After the long drought of 1976, Wessex Water plc bought the land at Tucking Mill from Laporte Industries Ltd and by 1980, a large pond covered the area once occupied by the fuller's earth works. This **reservoir** has a capacity of 15 million litres. In 1981, the 'Year of the Disabled', facilities were installed for the use of disabled anglers and the lake was stocked with a variety of coarse fish.

During an inspection of the site in December 1993, a brick marked 'Starworks **Glenboig**' was discovered. Among the records of the Fullers' Earth Union, there is correspondence in 1936 with the Glenboig Union Fire Clay Co. Ltd for 1,000 square bricks and one ton of ground fire clay. It was a long way to go for bricks and underlines the quality which that company produced: *'The superior quality of the high silica clays of the Glenboig* [north of Airdrie] *and Bonnybridge areas in the central belt* [of Scotland] *was discovered early on. Firebricks from these fields gained a world-wide reputation. Until recently Scotland dominated the world market for refractory ware.'* (Donnachie J., Hume J. & Moss M., *Historic Industrial Scenes – Scotland*, 1977)

BIBLIOGRAPHY

Addison, Peter, *Around Combe Down*, Millstream Books 1998
Arlett, M.J., *The Railways of Midford*, The Somerset & Dorset Trust 1983
Arlett, M.J., *The Somerset & Dorset at Midford*, Millstream Books 1986
Avon Industrial Buildings Trust, *Trail Guide to Tucking Mill*
Bladud Article op.cit.
Bodman, Martin, 'Mills on the Cam and Midford Brooks', *BIAS Journal*, No. 29, 1997
Broome, John, 'Tucking Mill', *BIAS Journal*, Vol. 20, 1988
Day, Joan, 'Views' (relating to the closing of Tucking Mill Fuller's Earth Works), *BIAS Journal*, Vol. 13, 1980
'Excursion to Bath, Midford (*et alia*) Whitsuntide 1893', *Proceedings of the Geologists Association*, Vol. 13, 1893
Pitcairn, Rev'd L., & Richardson, Rev'd A., *Historical Guide to Monkton Combe, Combe Down and Claverton*, 1924
Powell, John, 'Fullers Earth from Midford', *BIAS Journal*, Vol. 11, 1978
Sheppard, Thomas, *William Smith, His Maps and Memoirs*, 1920
Wicks, Stanley, 'I Remember Tucking Mill', Combe Down History Society 2007
Williams, W.J., & Stoddart, D.M., *Bath – Some Encounters with Science*, Kingsmead 1978

⊰ Chapter 5 ⊱

A WINDMILL ON ODD DOWN

And Other Local Ventures 1885-1904

EARLY MINING ON ODD DOWN

Although the first mining of fuller's earth at Odd Down may well date from Roman times, when they built their Fosse Way with its ditches on either side, it was only when Warner's map was published in 1810 that there is a definite indication of mining here, although the exact location is not clear. The area was surveyed in 1882-3 and when the OS map of 1884 was published, this did show two mines in the Odd Down area.

SOUTH STOKE WORKS, WANSDYKE

The first of these, a pit with a shaft reputed to be 60 feet (18m) deep, was alongside the Wansdyke, about halfway between Combe Hay Lane and the Cross Keys Inn on the Midford Road. This pit was known as 'Southstoke Works' and was owned by a Bath draper, W.H. Handley. A local workman, John ('Jono') Lambern, slipped on the steel plates and lost his arm when it was caught in the winding winch. Some drying of the blue earth may have taken place in the sheds here, shown in some detail on the 1886 OS map (1:2500). It has been said that it was abandoned due to flooding and it was marked as unused on the 1902 edition of the map.

The shaft was re-opened in September 2000 and found to be faced with Bath stone blocks to a depth of 8 feet (2.4m). This would have prevented the layer of brash rubble falling into the shaft and also provided a foundation for the winding gear. Some 22 feet (7m) of open shaft still remained, with much rubble blocking the horizontal galleries at the bottom of the shaft, which were known

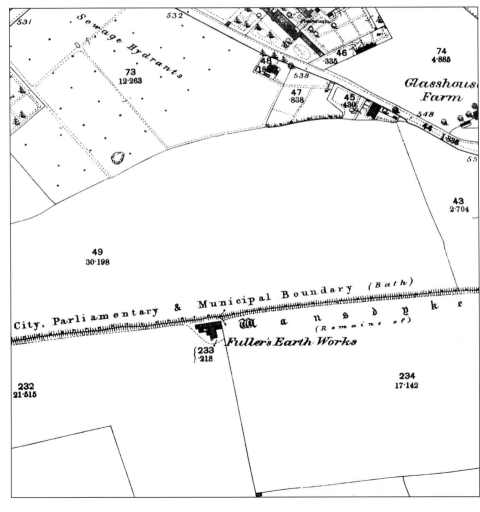

Wansdyke Mine, OS Map 1884. This mine on the Wansdyke was located approximately half way between Combe Hay Lane and the Cross Keys Inn. Extraction was by a vertical shaft. It is believed that flooding brought the operation to a premature end. On the OS 1903 edition it is noted as being disused.

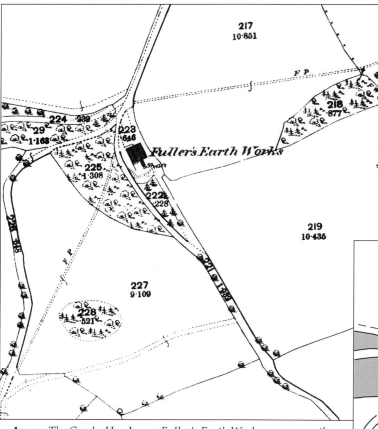

Above: The Combe Hay Lower Fuller's Earth Works appears on the OS 1884 edition map but not the Upper Works.

Right: Combe Hay Lower Works. These works were owned by Major Evan Butler and were in operation during the 1880s. It appears that he diverted the lane to Combe Hay so that it then passed to the west of his works. The old line of the lane may then have been used as an incline for the tramway from the adit. There were two shafts and an adit to the east of the works under the field known as 'Top Sowhills'. The next edition of the OS map (1903) showed the works as disused. Today, the foundations of the building in the old lane are still visible in the undergrowth and what appears to be the track formation of an incline can be traced down to the lower field.

at one time to exist to the west and southwest. The width of the track along the Wansdyke towards the Burnt House Inn suggests that the fuller's earth may have been taken out by this route.

COMBE HAY LOWER AND UPPER WORKS

There is a reference to these early mines in the *Proceedings of the Bath Natural History & Antiquarian Field Club*, entitled 'Walks and Bye Excursions 1885-86', although they are not very precise as to the exact locations:

'On March 24th [1885] *a walk was taken to the Fuller's Earth Works at Combe Hay, by Holloway*

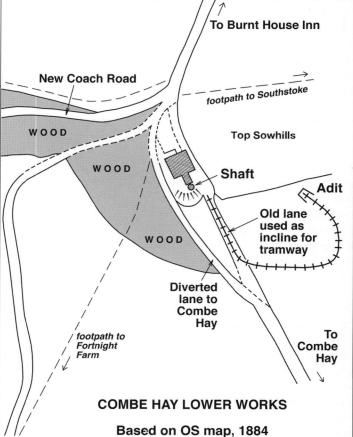

COMBE HAY LOWER WORKS

Based on OS map, 1884

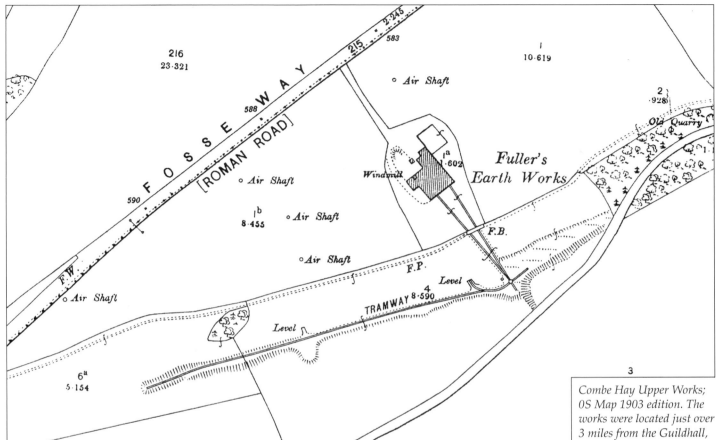

Combe Hay Upper Works; OS Map 1903 edition. The works were located just over 3 miles from the Guildhall, Bath at a height of 582ft (177m) above sea level. The presence of adits, air shafts and tramways suggest that, in the late 19th and early 20th centuries, the fuller's earth was being mined under the triangular field to the west of the works. Later, with the permission of the Duchy of Cornwall Estate, a tunnel was driven under the Fosse Way and the area north of this road and as far as the south side of Down Wood and Kilkenny Lane was exploited.

and Entry Hill; turning into the field opposite the Cross Keys and following the line of the Wansdyke to the road leading down to Combe Hay. On the left of the path the works which had originally existed here were abandoned, the 'tips' of blue clay alone indicating the site. On the right of the road a new opening had been made about 7 months ago, to a depth of some 17m [55ft] in the Great Oolite, by Mr Butler, the proprietor ... The works on the top of the rise opposite the newly made road to Combe Hay were still being carried on.'

To the east of the track to Combe Hay, two shafts were sunk; one, lined with bricks, was most likely for ventilation and a second, lined with blocks of Bath stone, could have been used for taking out some of the earth. The yellow fuller's earth was mainly extracted through adits using wheelbarrows and trestles. When Woodward wrote in 1894, he mentioned a shaft that was thirty feet deep and '*the opening of the tunnel showed yellow earth three feet or more in depth, which passes underground into blue earth, four or five feet thick.*' Was he referring to this mine? The site is marked on subsequent editions but

Large Scale Plan of Combe Hay Upper Works, c.1903. The relevant features of the windmill, engine house and kilns have been marked. The plan of the buildings would be that which pertained after extensive rebuilding in the final decade of the 19th century.

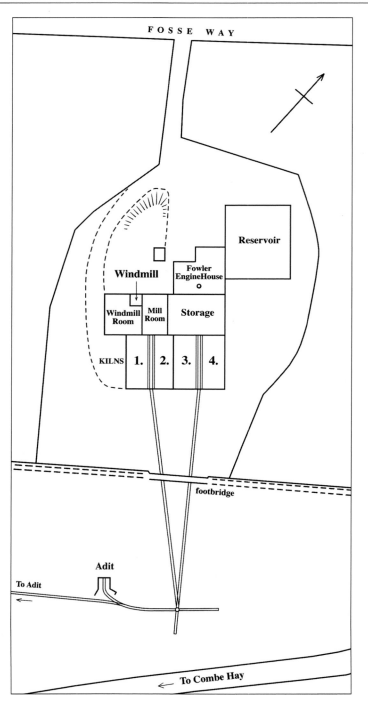

by then it was probably no longer producing fuller's earth. This mine, which may date from around 1881 and is sometimes called 'Combe Hay Lower Works', was owned by Major Samuel Evan Butler of Caisson House in Combe Hay. He also built the coach road down to that village in 1868.

Charlie Swatton has investigated the Lower Works over a number of years. It was owned and established by Major Butler by 1886 and appears to have been a split-level site separated by a 6 foot (1.8m) embankment. The main working area was on the lower level, where there were two buildings and the stone-lined shaft. The presence of ash and clinker indicates that there may have been a kiln and a small steam engine. On the upper level, in a triangular field, there was another building and the brick-lined shaft. A tramway led from the single adit up a steep incline to these works. It is possible that, although good yellow fuller's earth had been obtained at this site, it was closed about 1890 when the Upper Works were being developed and much of the stone and equipment may have been taken there.

Major Butler's father, Samuel Butler of the Manor House in Combe Hay, was lord of the manor and proprietor of the '*works which have been erected in this parish for the manufacture of 'fuller's earth', of which there is an extensive bed.*' He is listed in the mining records as the owner of Combe Hay Upper Works. These works were probably in existence by 1889. The Butlers, together with other producers of fuller's earth, formed the Fullers' Earth Union in March 1890. At that time, father and son appear to have been the joint owners of the Upper Works. The family continued to have an interest in the company in subsequent years, although it was not actively engaged in the extraction and processing of the earth. The area of the Upper Works was to prove the most significant site south of Bath. Here, fuller's earth was mined and processed for almost ninety years until closed in 1980. Much of it lies between the Combe Hay and Radstock roads on Picket Down, to the west, and Folly Down to the east, and the works first appears on the 1903 edition of the OS maps.

THE WINDMILL COMES AND GOES!

The 1902 map also shows a windmill, which became a remarkable landmark for a number of years. It was a Halladay & Wheeler Patent Windmill supplied by the United States Wind Engine and Pumping Engine Company of Batavia, Illinois. When it was brought from the United States, via Southampton, it is said to have cost as much to bring it from the docks to Bath as it had for the journey from Illinois! This was likely to have been soon after 1890, when the Fullers' Earth Union acquired the site and set about developing the buildings and plant that were already there. It was reputed to be the largest in the United Kingdom with its vanes some 50-60 feet (15-18m) in diameter and painted red, white and blue. The tower, with an overall height of around 75 feet (23m), was made of huge baulks of pitch pine and may well have been erected by the Southstoke firm of Clifford

Scene in England, showing one of Our 36-foot Diameter Halladay Wind Engines for Operating a Roller Grist Mill. Develops 12 Horse Power in an 18-mile wind.

Halladay Wind Engine. This photograph is from a catalogue of the U.S. Wind Engine & Pumping Co'y of Batavia, Illinois, dating from about 1905. The only clue as to the site is the name of the Midland Railway on the flatbed horse-drawn wagons. The whole scene is very reminiscent of that which would have been seen at the windmill site on Odd Down at the end of the 19th century.
T. Lindsay Baker

Brothers, which did other building work for the Union. The building which housed the mill machinery formed the base for the windmill structure. It had a tiled roof and was floored with Staffordshire blue bricks, and there are signs of pillars which may have supported the base of the windmill, which measured 12 feet (3.6m) square. The windmill butted onto a smaller building which housed the hoist for loading the carts.

The windmill was used to drive a grinding mill, although a steam engine was available to provide power when necessary for the mill and blender. This engine, No. 5880, had been manufactured by John Fowler & Son of Leeds and was possibly installed at the same time as the

ABOVE: The Windmill. This photograph shows all the vanes in place, which are casting shadows on the mill buildings. There is a horse and cart to the right of the picture and there is no building on the right side of the boiler house, which has two doors. This may be the earliest photograph in existence, probably dating from well before 1900.

RIGHT: The Windmill. Again all the vanes are in place and the boiler is in use. The chimney is the same as above. The photograph was taken by J.A. Howe from the lane leading in to the works from the Fosse Way. Below the windmill, a winch and a horse-operated winding drum can be seen in front of the building.

Windmill at Odd Down

windmill, to provide an alternative source of power and for the haulage of trams up the incline from the early adits. There would be days when there was insufficient wind for the giant vanes or when maintenance had to be carried out. Local coal, and coke supplied by the Bath Gas Light & Coke Company, would have been used for the boiler and kilns. The boiler had an iron chimney, constructed in 10 foot (3m) sections, 2.5 feet (0.75m) in diameter and some 90 feet (27m) tall with a crown on the top. Power was transmitted to the machinery in the works by a system of drive belts and pulley wheels on a long shaft which ran the whole length of the mill buildings.

Early photographs of the works suggest that the windmill was an integral part of the structure rather than something added at a later date. The windmill differed from the usual four-bladed arrangement of sails in that it had annular vanes and was called a 'wind engine', the power generated being proportional to the area swept by the vanes. According to Stuart Burroughs, the advantage of the annular type of wind engine lay in the lightness of the components used. The wind wheel pivoted atop a light steel tower clad with wooden weather-boarding and the speed of the wheel was automatically governed by equipment which, in times of high winds, could turn the sails or vanes 'out of the wind'. Power was transmitted directly to the machinery below via a vertical shaft. It was due to this landmark that the works were known locally as the 'Windmill Works'.

In his article on these windmills, Dr T. Lindsay Baker wrote '*Behind the large wind wheel, which was fitted with variable-pitch blades, was a fan tail mounted at a right angle to the principal wheel. This fan tail was so arranged through connection with the mill that its turning blades held the main wheel facing the wind at all times. Through the use of a centrifugal governor, the individual blades composing the wind wheel were changed in pitch to give the mill a more-or-less regular operating speed.*' They were manufactured from about 1870 until the turn of the 20th century. By September 1903, the windmill was no longer in use and a photograph shows a new chimney being put up, which was shorter and had a spark-arrester on the top.

Six months later, on the night of Monday 29th February 1904, the windmill was burnt down. This was fully reported in the local papers. The report in the *Bath Journal* did not give a date for the erection of the wind engine but said that it had cost £3,000, and '*… although found useful at first, the difficulties of obtaining sufficient wind on some occasions led to it being abandoned in favour of steam power and the sails were removed but the iron and woodwork remained.*'

The *Bath Chronicle* reported that the fire apparently broke out in the shed where the sacks were

The Windmill. All the vanes have been removed and a new chimney, which is tapered and of larger diameter, is being erected. The framed print has written on the back 'New chimney fixed up Sept 1903. Windmill burnt down Mar 1904. Frame made from pitch pine, part of the sails recovered from the fire'. This had been written by Dick Clifford.
ROGER CLIFFORD

stored and by the time the horse-drawn fire brigade engine arrived from the centre of Bath:

> '… the flames had a firm hold on the wooden supports of the wheel. As the tower creaked and tottered the situation became extremely dangerous for those engaged in the work of extinction and of preventing the conflagration spreading to the rest of the premises. At one time the wheel inclined considerably to the east and it appeared as if it would fall that way. Had it done so it would have wrought much damage as it must have crashed through into the adjoining building where the engine and machinery are located. But suddenly a heavy gust of wind sprang up from the south-east and the wheel gave its final revolution westwards and landed on clear ground, where it now lies a complete wreck.'

By 2am on Tuesday 1st March, the three officers and fifteen men of the brigade were able to stop fighting the fire. The report in the *Bath Chronicle* continued:

> 'The residents of Odd Down and frequentors of the main road to Radstock and Wells have lost a familiar and prominent landmark … seen and noticed for many miles around. Standing as it did on one of the highest and barest parts of the Odd Down plateau it was especially conspicuous … The wheel was composed, like its supports, principally of wood but a heavy iron cylindrical cog formed part of the structure and had it come down the other side the engines would have been smashed … The works generally are unaffected by the fire and operations are proceeding as usual.'

The premises were insured with the Northern Fire Office, much to the relief of the manager Mr W.F. Keevil. Fortunately, there was a reservoir on the north-east side of the works, the Bath & District Water Company having agreed with the Fullers' Earth Union for a supply of water to the works in April 1893. This would have proved invaluable on the night of the fire. Dick Clifford salvaged a piece of pitch pine from the remains and used it to make a frame for the photograph which shows the chimney surrounded with scaffolding. After the fire, in which part of the roof was destroyed, a temporary roof of half round sheet iron plates was installed. This remained for a number of years until the whole works were re-roofed.

OTHER LOCAL SMALL MINING VENTURES

Very little is known about three small mining ventures which were located on Rush Hill at Odd Down, Hodshill at Southstoke, and around Wellow. They all existed before the Fullers' Earth Union was founded in 1890.

RUSH HILL

According to Charlie Swatton, Evergreen Cottage and its buildings at Rush Hill may well be the first place where fuller's earth was both dug and processed in the Bath area. In 1861, a John Holloway, who lived at Odd Down Cottages, gave his occupation as 'fuller's earth miner'. As Evergreen Cottage dates from this time, or even earlier, he may have been employed at Evergreen Fuller's Earth Works.

Evergreen Cottage, Rush Hill. A view of the cottage from the east. The stone set in the wall is in the corner to the right of the ground floor windows.
AUTHOR

The earth was dug by open cast methods from a pit or shallow quarry some 100 yards long by 25 yards wide (91m by 23m) , just to the west of St Philip's church at Odd Down. This accounts for the green area in front of the houses on the north side of the road at the top of Rush Hill. Clods of wet earth would have been sold directly, although some drying could have taken place by spreading them on a shed floor. The Evergreen pit did not last long; the deposits were no longer being worked when, eventually, this small concern was bought by Cawley & Co. Ltd around 1890, having previously held the leasehold.

Evergreen Cottage, which was occupied by the manager W.A. Sheppard, still stands near the site. His initials and the date 1885 are carved on a stone at the back of the cottage.

Walter Allen Sheppard was listed as a quarrymaster at Evergreen Cottage in Odd Down in the 1884/85 *Bath Directory*, while the edition of 1886/7 mentioned him at Fuller's Earth Works at the same location. The next edition has him living at Bloomfield Crescent and as the proprietor of Fuller's Earth Works without specifying its location. His last association with the industry seems to have been when he was listed in 1890/91 as the manager of Fuller's Earth Works and living at Cleve Hill House in Midford. As mentioned previously, it is possible that at that time he may have been managing the nearby works at Tucking Mill for H.N. Garrett.

WELLOW

An advertisement appeared in the *Bath Chronicle* of 7th April 1803, concerning a fulling mill at Stoney Littleton near Wellow which was for sale or to be let. It was on four floors with a water wheel, machinery and two fulling stocks *'for manufacturing eight to ten cloths per week'*. As mentioned earlier, the Rev'd John Skinner, Rector of the nearby parish of Camerton in the early years of that century, wrote in his Journal of the soil at Wellow *'being constantly turned up by the clothiers in search of the earth'*, where he was investigating the Roman villa. This might indicate the presence of small pits in the area at that time.

The early history of fuller's earth at Wellow is not well documented. It appears that around 1886 or 1887, a Mr Candy, who may have been responsible for constructing the building for drying the earth in the centre of the village in 1884, sold the Wellow Fuller's Earth Works to Claude William Cawley. Cawley & Co. Ltd then owned both the works at Wellow and Evergreen. The company had the power to mine under other adjacent lands as well as having the freehold of the Wellow mines. In 1890, Cawley sold to the Fullers' Earth Union, of which he was one of the founding

1902 6ins OS map of the Wellow Area. The map shows the two sites where fuller's earth was mined. To the north of the village a tramway led from Bath Hill House to the adit in the field known as 'The Hayes', whilst to the south, a tramway led from Hassage Hill to the adit. The fuller's earth works were in the centre of the village alongside the railway.

members, and H.N. Garrett leased it from the Union.

The local directory of 1894/95 for Wellow shows that Garrett was the occupier of a tenement on Baggridge Hill, although his residence was in the centre of Bath. For a while it is likely that he was managing both Wellow and Tucking Mill, as it would have been an easy matter to commute between the two sites by the Somerset & Dorset Joint Railway. A time-book records that, from December 1892 at least and until January 1894, Garrett was managing the Wellow Fuller's

This photograph from c.1884 is reputed to have been taken during the construction of the Wellow Fuller's Earth Works building, in the centre of the village adjacent to the Somerset & Dorset Joint Railway.
GORDON HEWLETT AND THE ARCHIVES OF THE WELLOW HISTORICAL SOCIETY

Earth Works and his foreman was James Palmer. There were six men and a night stoker. The latter was Frank Palmer who also worked days. It seems likely that the Fullers' Earth Union may have leased these works to Garrett for a period. From 4th January 1894, Garrett decided to concentrate all his efforts at Tucking Mill. James Palmer and his wife were Wellow people, they were born and married there and they moved into Tucking Mill house about 1895. His brother Frank was also on the books and had tended the fires at night at Wellow. Garrett also took several other men from Wellow to work at Midford. It has been suggested that he abandoned Wellow because the workable seams of fuller's earth there were too thin, whereas those in Horsecombe Vale were proving successful.

Again, he required ground fuller's earth because he wanted to enter the expanding American oil refining market and there may have been no grinding facilities at Wellow. At Midford he could produce the quality of washed and refined earth that the oil industry required.

The Reports of the Government Inspector of Mines indicate that earth was being produced at Wellow from at least 1887 and that it continued until 1892. The *Bath Directory* for 1904 lists W.F. Keevil as the manager at Wellow, as well as at Combe Hay, but this does not prove that any mining was still taking place there. Another article suggests that, around the turn of the century, activity at Wellow ceased and prior to that date,

Wellow Fuller's Earth Works. The building as seen from the north in 1988.
TONY BROWN

TOP: Wellow Fuller's Earth Works. The south elevation taken from the track bed of the former Somerset & Dorset Joint Railway. Railway wagons could have been loaded directly from the opening above the windows. This may also have been the entrance for an aerial ropeway from Hassage Hill if, in fact, such existed.
TONY BROWN

MIDDLE: Wellow Fuller's Earth Works. The main doorway on the south side of the building.
TONY BROWN

BOTTOM: Wellow Fuller's Earth Works. One of the four cast iron furnace doors in the west wall of the building.
TONY BROWN

a Mr Colbourne was managing the works. The building in the centre of Wellow was then converted to a blacksmith, wheelwright and waggon-building business, which continued until the introduction of modern lorries. The 60 feet (18m) high chimney on the mill was taken down around 1964.

The fuller's earth was brought from a field to the north of the village, known as 'The Hayes', by a tram track to the road at Bath Hill House. From there, a horse and cart would have taken the earth to the mill in the centre of the village. There had been a large Roman villa surrounded by almost 800 acres (330 hectares) of land to the west of Bath Hill on the same contour level as the mine where earth was later dug. The mine in that area later became a rubbish dump but it was still known as 'the fuller's earth ground'.

Fuller's earth was also mined to the south of Wellow on Hassage Hill. Again, a tramway led to the road to the village, although it has been suggested that there was a system of buckets on an aerial ropeway from Hassage Hill direct to the mill in the centre of the village. As at Tucking Mill, the earth was dried on steel plates with flues under the floor. The four doors of the kilns are still to be seen on the west side of the building. There is no record of any other process being carried on here. The first floor level hatch on the south side of the building could have been for loading directly into railway wagons or, as some have suggested, to receive buckets from an aerial ropeway from Hassage Hill, if in fact such existed. The mill was conveniently sited alongside the Somerset & Dorset Joint Railway, possibly with a siding to transport the finished product to distant markets. It was the most prestigious building built in this area for the fuller's earth industry but sadly mining in this district was short-lived, despite the fact that there are still large deposits of earth in the region of Twinhoe, between Wellow and Midford.

The OS revised map of 1902 shows both the Fuller's Earth Works to the north west and south of Wellow as disused and although the mill in the centre of the village is shown, it is not identified as having any connection with this industry.

SOUTH STOKE AT HODSHILL

Mining did not last very long at Hodshill either. Jeremy Hignett, who once lived in Hodshill Hall, found traces of an adit south of the house in 'Little Hodshill Field', while to the west there was a quarry which produced very good freestone. He thought some of the stone might have been used for the locks on the canal at Combe Hay. He noted that there was very little spoil associated with the adit probably because, as Henry Tanner has pointed out, the main extraction was by the open cast method. The workings may not have been very extensive and there was no sign of the ground above sinking, so any adit must have been well supported. Hodshill workings were alleged to have been in operation from 1886 until 1894 but the official mining records say it stopped in 1892. The 1904 map shows the site of the abandoned adits or workings as a quarry. The army used the old workings as a rifle range during the First World War.

From the workings a tramway ran south across Cottage Field on a slightly raised clay embankment towards the fuller's earth works. Here there were two rectangular

Left: Wellow Station. Looking towards Midford, the chimney of the fuller's earth works adjacent to the railway can be clearly seen. J.H. Moss

Below: Wellow Fuller's Earth Works. Two sketches prepared by the author in 1988 showing the positions of the furnace doors and the hole in the roof left by the chimney.

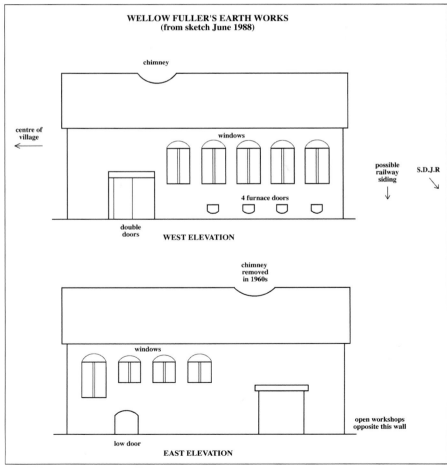

WELLOW FULLER'S EARTH WORKS
(from sketch June 1988)

chimney

centre of village →

windows

4 furnace doors

double doors

WEST ELEVATION

possible railway siding ↓

S.D.J.R ↓

chimney removed in 1960s

windows

low door

open workshops opposite this wall

EAST ELEVATION

1884 25in OS for Hodshill, annotated by J.J. Hignett. Mining took place on the south side of Hodshill and a tramway across Cottage Field led directly to what is now Underhill Cottage. It was here that any processing of the earth took place before being despatched, possibly by the Somersetshire Coal Canal, a short distance away.

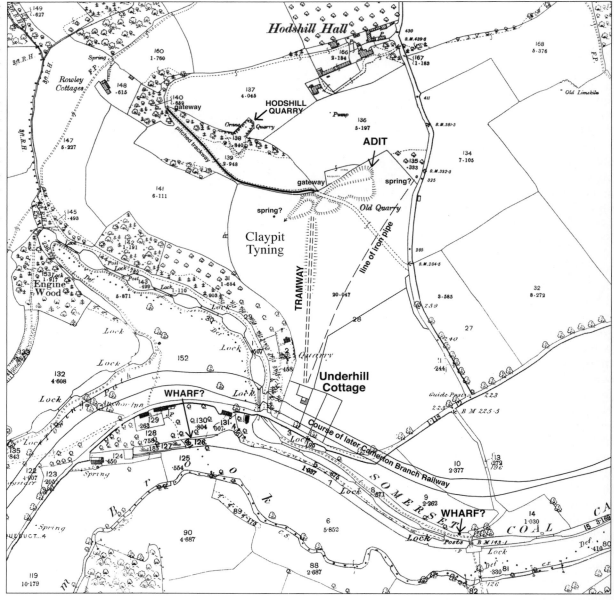

settlement tanks and a pipeline from a spring supplied water, possibly for making the earth into a slurry. There were two drying ovens or kilns in the bank towards the rear of the building, with four furnace doors. Milling to provide a finer powder took place in the building later known as Underhill Cottage but Jack Clifford did not think that there had been any slurrying of the earth as at Tucking Mill, rather it was simply dried and ground.

It is not clear how the finished product was transported from the works to the Somersetshire Coal Canal, a short distance below. There have been suggestions that there was an inclined tramway from Underhill Cottage down to the lane but evidence of this has been obliterated by the later building of the railway embankment. There was a track, shown on the 1840 tithe map, from Bridge Farm to Glen Cottage, which lies a little way up the valley from Underhill Cottage. A large stone gatepost near the old railway bridge marks its lower point. Could this have been the route used to transport earth to the canal? Hignett, along with others, thought that the finished fuller's earth might have been loaded at a wharf near Anchor Farm, off the Midford to Combe Hay lane. Jack Clifford said that the finished earth was taken in sacks down what he called 'the dark path', to the pound on the canal near the Southstoke accommodation bridge. He maintained that there was a crane there to load the earth which had been brought by horse and cart from Underhill. There is indeed a substantial masonry platform still standing next to the canal at this point, although some have questioned the suitability of such a site for loading barges. The canal could also have brought coal for the kilns from higher up the Cam Valley but the declining state of the canal in the late 1880s would not have helped the Hodshill enterprise.

Some confusion also surrounds mining in Southstoke since the short-lived mine on the Wansdyke, referred to above, and that at Hodshill both lie in the parish of Southstoke. Uriah Handley, living at Hodshill Lodge, clearly was in charge at the Hodshill mine from 1886-91 when, according to the directories, he is listed as the manager. W.H. Handley lived at Hodshill House (later Hodshill Hall) and is recorded as the owner of Southstoke mine, which could be either Wansdyke or Hodshill, or both. His company was known as 'The Minerals & Mining Company'. A postcard from Uriah Handley in the Bowler correspondence at the Museum of Bath at Work, dated 16th July 1888, stated that he was going to bring gas burners to Bowler's Brass Foundry in Corn Street in the centre of Bath, presumably for some attention or replacement. Jack Clifford remembered that it was said by the proprietor of the Hodshill Works that, when the first load of fuller's earth was mined and sold, '*Every woman in the parish could be measured for a piece of material for a dress*'. This could well have been W.H. Handley, who was a draper! Underhill Cottage was converted to a dwelling in 1911 and completely renovated in the 1970s, and there is no trace of its original use.

NOTES TO CHAPTER 5

The Windmill. The following is taken from Owen Ward's article 'Serious Fire on Odd Down' in a Conference Paper for The International Molinological Society, at the 10th International Symposium on Molinology, Stratford Hall, Virginia, U.S.A. 16-24th Sept. 2000. He suggests that if money was quickly subscribed in 1890 (at the formation of the FEU):

'*... this would have enabled the new Union to get on with the task of constructing and equipping their range of workshops, including the wind engine, which could have been erected some time in 1891 at the latest. There could be several reasons why an American model wind engine was selected. One convincing suggestion is that one or other of the English producers, not necessarily from the Bath end of the new business, already had contacts with the American oil extraction and processing industry which made extensive use of fuller's earth. Such a connection seems the more likely as the Fullers' Earth Union shrewdly acquired fuller's earth reserves in Arkansas only a few years later, in 1897.*'

He thinks the price of the wind engine is more likely to have been around £300 not £3,000, as the 1897 catalogue of the company quotes the price of a 36ft wind engine as $1,000. '*The wooden tower would have been put up by the FEU, since Halladays expected purchasers to have, or to build, their own support to suit their own purposes.*' Referring to the report in the press of the fire which destroyed the windmill, he also points out that the reference to the '*Northern Fire Office*' is not enough to identify the company concerned but the Northern Accident Insurance Co. Ltd, based in Glasgow, had an agent in Bath in the 1890s. He was Henry Coward of the City Bank.

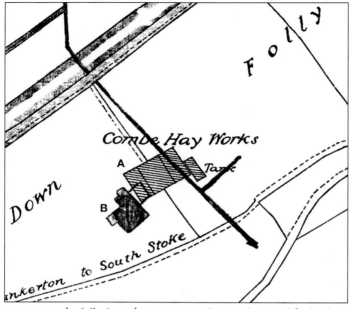

The Combe Hay Lower Fuller's Earth Works appears on the **Ordnance Survey** 1884 edition map but not the Upper Works. The Wansdyke Fuller's Earth Works appears on the same edition but on the 1904 edition it is noted as being disused.

The **ancient lane** which leaves Combe Hay lane near the Combe Hay Lower Works was altered by Major S. Evan Butler so that it swept in a curve round to the west of these Works.

The Fullers' Earth Union owned two plots of land adjacent to the **Somersetshire Coal Canal** in the parish of Combe Hay. One, a small plot at ST733602, would have been reached by the path which left the track south of Fortnight Farm, the other stood next to the lane leading past the Lower Works from the village. The land may have been part of the Butler estate prior to the formation of the Fullers' Earth Union and it is possible that he, or later the Company, hoped to use the canal to transport the fuller's earth to customers. It is not known if the land was ever used for this purpose.

A study of two old, undated, **Fullers' Earth Union maps** at the Bath Royal Literary & Scientific Institution, which are based on the OS 1884 map, shows the Combe Hay Upper Fuller's Earth Works on Picket and Folly Downs and the Lower Works off Combe Hay Lane:

1. The Cloth Map: Both works are labelled and shaded with the same hatching which suggests that both may have been in operation. The Upper Works is shown as a plain rectangle building (A), which is not aligned parallel to the Fosse Way, with a tank in the south east corner. A lane leads in from the road. Adjacent to this building another building (B) to the south west has been added more crudely. It resembles in outline the complete works as shown on the OS 1903 map. The map has a number of obviously later annotations, *e.g. 'Clapham Junction District. It was here that we were troubled with bad air during September and beginning of Oct.'; 'West Road District (now abandoned)'*, referring to a large underground area to the north west of the works. Both are in the handwriting of one of the Keevil managers. Long underground roadways which were driven in the 20th century are clearly shown. All these additions indicate that the map was used and annotated for some time after it was originally produced.

2. The Second Map: Appears to have been drawn later, has *'Magnetic Meridian Sept. 1914'* marked on the compass logo. The map shows early underground workings in the immediate vicinity of the Upper Works and underneath the large original building (A). The crudely drawn building (B) has now been redrawn more accurately, with the lane now leading directly to this building. The Lower Works building is no longer hatched or labelled; it was clearly no longer in use.

An analysis of these maps suggests that the building (A) was completely demolished by 1903 and the lane from the Fosse Way (A367) leading to it replaced by another leading to building (B). This building was in fact the basis of those buildings which remain today.

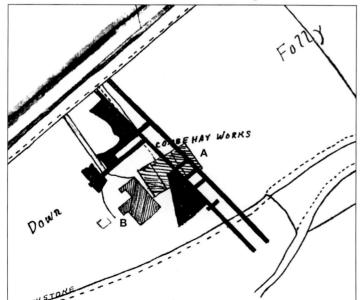

In the Rolt Memorial Lecture, 1990, 'Wind Engines' by J. Kenneth Major, published in *Industrial Archaeology Review Vol. XIV No. 1*, Autumn 1991, Major noted that '*The 1893 Exposition in Chicago had an invited "field" of wind engines, which from the photograph,* [presumably this refers to one taken at the exposition but not included in the above publication] *all appear to be American.*' He refers to the article by Alfred R. Wolff, 'The Windmill as Prime Mover', first published in 1885 and again in 1894. The Company was present at the Exhibition, where it won the highest award for its fuller's earth products. The Company exhibited again at St. Louis, Missouri, in 1904. Major points out that '*John Wallis Titt of Warminster, Wiltshire was producing wind engines from the 1880s and were mostly fitted with shuttered annular sails.*'

Wind engines were displayed especially during the 1880s at the Royal Agricultural Society of England annual shows. Halladay models were displayed at Newcastle in 1887, Windsor 1889, and Warwick 1892. Hence the Fullers' Earth Union could have been familiar with these particular models as well as other makes before making a decision to purchase a Halladay engine from the USA, probably around 1891.

True fuller's earth was discovered near Alexander, Arkansas in 1891 by John Olsen. Robertson says that the Fullers' Earth Union acquired Olsen's fuller's earth mine at **Klondyke, Arkansas** in 1911 and that it was run by Owen Keevil for a while. It is possible he was there for about a year as we know he was back in the United Kingdom by c.1912.

In an article by a member of the Bath Field Club on William Smith in the *Bath Chronicle*, 9th April 1874, entitled 'How the Study of Stratigraphical Geology Commenced Near Bath', it was noted that '*Fuller's Earth … is not so extensively employed as formerly, but the shafts near the back of **Rush Hill** are still worked to obtain it …*'. No other works are mentioned, although '*… at Week, Fortnight and Three Days are excellent exposures where its character can be examined …*'. These are the names of a group of farms (which still exist) in Combe Hay, just below the sites exploited soon after by the Combe Hay Lower and Upper Works.

Walter Allen Sheppard had a wide-ranging career including being a haulier, steam traction owner and road builder. From the 1890s onward, he was proprietor of Roadite Ltd, Traction Engine & Road Rolling Contractors, which he eventually ran from offices in Milsom Street. In the early 1920s, he served as City Councillor on the Surveying Committee and was active in promoting white-lining and other innovations onto the Bath roads. He lived into his 90s.

Bowler's Foundry. J.B. Bowler, Engineer and Brass Founder, at 12-13 Corn Street in the centre of Bath, was a well-established business. Its collection of equipment and artefacts formed the basis of the Bath at Work Museum. Cawley & Co. was a customer of Bowler at least by October 1890. The Fullers' Earth Union Ltd became a customer by December 1891 and for many years afterwards, and when the firm became J.B. Bowler & Sons in 1912. It remained in existence until the 1960s.

Formation of the Fullers' Earth Union Ltd. In the Prospectus, Evergreen (leasehold) and Wellow (freehold) were purchased from Cawley & Co. Ltd on 4th Feb. 1890, although '*Evergreen Works are not now carried on*'. Southstoke (freehold) was purchased from W.H. Handley on 8th Feb. 1890 and '*Beds of Earth at Midford*' (leasehold) from G. Dames on 25th Feb. 1890. It appears from the Prospectus that some of the local owners, *i.e.* Cawley, (Wellow and Evergreen), and Handley, (Southstoke), and Dames, (beds of fuller's earth), first sold their interest to the Mineral & Fullers' Earth Syndicate Ltd, so negotiations were carried on with the Syndicate. '*The Contract for the sale of all the Properties* [*i.e.* Wellow, Southstoke and Evergreen at Odd Down] *to the Company* [*i.e.* the Fullers' Earth Union Ltd] *is dated the 18th day of March, and is made between the Mineral & Fullers' Earth Syndicate, Ltd, of the one part, and Charles Edward Thomas as Trustee for the Company of the other part*'. The Union aimed to inflate the price of earth by doing away with '*ill judged*' competition, hence the amalgamation of the three Surrey and six Bath works. In 1890, the total output was 12,000 tons.

According to the *Bath Chronicle*, 3rd Nov. 1892, there was a General Meeting of the Shareholders of the Fullers' Earth Union on 31st Oct. 1892 at the Cannon Street Hotel, London. It was noted that depression in trade had occurred and the cost of production had risen. It had been a time of severe competition and woollen manufactories were '*in a deplorably depressed condition*'. The Union had been formed for the purpose of lowering the cost of production and present prospects were much improved and sales had increased. Commenting on the Yorkshire woollen trade, Bill Bryson in *Notes from a Small Island*, 1994, noted that '*In 1893 the textile trade went into a sudden slump, leaving the Salts* [Titus Salt Jnr. at Saltaire in Airedale, between Bingley and Shipley] *dangerously over extended, and the family lost control of the firm*'.

It was noted by Greenwood, however, that '*In an attempt to prevent further price cutting amongst themselves, the Somerset manufacturers formed marketing organisations, first the London Fuller's Earth Co. Ltd. and then in January 1890 the Minerals & Fullers' Earth Syndicate Ltd. at the same London address as its predecessor.* [The latter company had its registered office in Bath according to Robertson.] *Although the activities of this latter company were soon overtaken by events, it was not dissolved until 1911 and several of its small number of shareholders were also involved with the Fullers' Earth Union Ltd. The role of William Blewitt, an Essex solicitor, but also a director of the London & General Bank, in the formation of this new venture is somewhat indeterminate, but he was significantly the only major shareholder in the three enterprises of Cawley & Co., the Minerals & Fullers'*

Earth Syndicate Ltd. and the Fullers' Earth Union Ltd. and was a possible source of finance.'

The Fullers' Earth Union only completed their ownership of all the mines in Somerset and Surrey with that of Beechfield Works, Surrey in 1919. The Prospectus also shows that there were nearly a hundred shareholders, many of whom were prominent in Bath, such as the 2-stroke inventor Joseph Day, the Rev'd C.W. Shickle, historian and Master of St John's Hospital, the building firm Hayward & Wooster, and members of the Coward family of engineers.

Wellow: Stony Littleton Mill. According to K.H. Rogers in his book on local woollen mills, *'Nothing is known of the woollen trade here before 1812, when a manufactory called Littleton Mill was offered for sale with the new-improved machinery for carrying on the clothing business or working for hire. A water-wheel worked two pairs of stocks and drums and shafts for gigs and shearing frames. The machinery, which included two gigs, ten Daniell's patent shearing frames and eight Daniell's patent looms, was offered for sale shortly afterwards. The mill was only called a fulling mill when it was offered for sale in 1828, and was still so described in 1840; it was then, however, occupied by a farmer, and had probably stopped work. Nothing remains on the site.'* Rogers was obviously unaware of the reference in the *Bath Chronicle* quoted above. His references were from the *Salisbury & Winchester Journal*, 15th June 1812, and *Devizes & Wiltshire Gazette*, 18th Sept. 1828.

The 1891 Census for Wellow lists an Edward Holvey and Henry Frapwell as 'Fuller's Earth Miner'. Both George Staddon, aged 55, and his son Thomas, aged 27, are listed as 'engine driver stationary' and another son Henry, aged 17, as a 'fuller's earth labourer'. A number of the Staddon family worked in the fuller's earth industry. George and Thomas may therefore have been responsible for the steam engine at Odd Down or possibly at Wellow.

A note is recorded in the minutes of Wellow Parish Council 18th May 1897: *'The following needs to be done; 1) The Fullers Earth Co. be requested to metal the section from Bath Hill to the gate below Dr Thompson's and the ground inside the gateway near their tipping place. 2) The District Council be asked to insist upon the Fullers Earth Co. making the bridge which they had constructed of a far less temporary character.'*

Later, on 10th June, the *Bath Chronicle* reported: *'Bath Town Council records a memorial from Wellow Parish Council suggesting that the Fullers Earth Works Co. be called upon to make good a path and bridge approaches at Bath Hill. The Surveyor said the bridge appeared to him to be safe. The approaches, however, were unsatisfactory and he had seen Mr. Keevil representing the Fuller's Earth on the matter. He had offered to do what was requisite to the path and approaches. The bridge, which has cost £40 to put up, he thought strong enough to bear 10 tons weight. The surveyor was asked to see the work was carried out.'*

BIBLIOGRAPHY
Report of the Windmill Fire; *Bath Chronicle*, Thurs. 3rd March1904, and *Bath Journal* Sat. 5th March1904
Article, 'The Halladay Wind Engine', *The Engineer*, August 1896
Baker, Dr T.L., 'Halladay and Wheeler's Patent Windmill', *Old Mills News*, XXIII, No. 3 (Summer 1994), Society for the Preservation of Old Mills
'Walks and Bye Excursions 1885-86', *Proceedings of the Bath Natural History & Antiquarian Field Club*, Vol. 6 1889
Burroughs, Stuart, 'Some thoughts on the Halladay and Wheeler's Patent Windmill installed at the Fuller's Earth Works, Bath', *The Survey of Bath and District* No. 10, Survey of Old Bath. October 1998
Burroughs, Stuart, 'The Odd Down Windmill', *Bath Industrial Heritage Trust Newsletters*, October 1998 and January 1999
Chapman, Mike, 'The Canal and the Fuller's Earth Mines at Combe Hay', *The Weigh-House* (newsletter of the Somersetshire Coal Canal Society) No. 45, May 2006
Greenwood, Jeremy, *Fullers Earth in Surrey 1500-1900, An Economic History*, published privately, 1983
Laidlaw, Philip, 'Windmills – Old and New', *Strand Magazine*, 1898
Major, J. Kenneth, 'The Windmills of John Wallis Titt', *TIMS*, 1977
Mullins, Donald, Article on Fuller's Earth in *Somerset Countryman*, Vol. 17, 1951-53, No. 11, July-Sept. 1953
Rogers, K.H., *Wiltshire and Somerset Woollen Mills*, Pasold Research Fund Ltd., Edington, 1976
Wolff, Alfred R., *The Windmill as a Prime Mover*, New York 1890
Woodward, H.B., 'The Jurassic Rocks of Britain', *Memoirs of the Geological Survey of the United Kingdom*, Vol. IV, 1894, HMSO

H.M. Inspector of Mines Records:
The Mining Statistics of The United Kingdom of Great Britain & Ireland with the Isle of Man 1888-1896
Mines and Quarries: General Report and Statistics United Kingdom 1897-1914
Report of the Secretary for Mines 1913ff
List of Mines in Great Britain (under the Metalliferous Mines Regulation Act), HMSO 1922
Mining and Mineral Statistics (Clay Section)
Home Office List of Quarries in the United Kingdom (under the Quarries Act 1894) HMSO

⊰❊ **Chapter 6** ❊⊱

KILNS AND CRUSHERS

Early Years on Odd Down 1890-1940

THE PLANT AND PROCESSING AT COMBE HAY WORKS

It seems that at the start of mining operations on Picket and Folly Downs, located on the southern border of Odd Down, all extraction was confined to the east side of the Fosse Way, as the land on the other side belonged to the Duchy of Cornwall. Eventually in the early years of the 20th century, permission was obtained to dig earth in this area as well. During the period that the processing works operated, there were changes in the machinery and methods of processing the fuller's earth from the mines and open cast sites.

By 1914, the Fowler steam engine equipment was in desperate need of replacement, as it had been in continual use since the fire destroyed the windmill in 1904. Owing to wartime restrictions, it was impossible to replace it despite the fact that the industry was vital to the war effort. It is also possible that a 'Niagara' Crusher and Pulverizer, which was patented by W.H. Coward and manufactured by Messrs Easton, Anderson & Goolden Ltd, was in use in the closing years of the 19th

Niagara Crusher and Pulverizer. The Niagara Mill or Crusher was patented by W.H. Coward of Railway Place in Bath before 1892. He described it as 'A rapid Pulverizer for Hard, Gritty Substances'. It may be that this crusher was installed at the Windmill site in the early days, especially as there is a reference in the Prospectus to better machinery being installed. Robertson and Torrens have both considered this a possibility, as it was claimed that by 1895, by which time Messrs Easton, Anderson & Goolden Ltd at Erith Works had become the sole manufacturers, it had successfully crushed fuller's earth amongst other materials.
FROM THE MACHINERY MARKET, 2ND DEC., 1895, P.418F

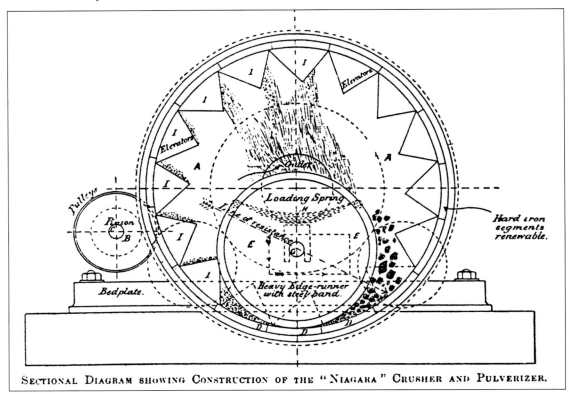

SECTIONAL DIAGRAM SHOWING CONSTRUCTION OF THE "NIAGARA" CRUSHER AND PULVERIZER.

century. After he left Bath, George Dames used such a crusher in the fuller's earth works at Apsley Heath in Bedfordshire. This crusher was particularly suited to crushing or grinding the fuller's earth. It ran slowly and could be adjusted to make anything from granules to fine powders. The company installed a new mill in 1913. A 3.25hp paraffin oil engine made by Crossley Brothers Ltd of Manchester, referred to in June 1917, may have been used for electric lighting. The surviving records, which are incomplete and date from 1915, give some idea of the operations and plant in use from that time onwards.

At the end of the First World War, there were a number of improvements to the plant and buildings. In 1918, a new boiler and steam engine were ordered. A Garrett CCSV II 170 h.p. superheated, semi-stationary steam engine was bought from Richard Garrett & Sons Ltd at Leiston in Suffolk, later a branch of Beyer, Peacock & Co. Ltd, and installed in the summer of 1919. This plant was the first of its kind in the area and it required the building of an annexe onto the north-west side of the existing engine house. The manager, Owen Keevil, hoped that once the new boiler was installed production would return to the level of pre-war days. He noted that the

Memorandum on the Niagara Crusher by W.H. Coward, 1892.
FULLER'S EARTH ARCHIVES AT THE MUSEUM OF BATH AT WORK

W.H.Coward's bill head, dated 1887, with illustrations of their works at Railway Place and Broad Quay.
MUSEUM OF BATH AT WORK

works at Combe Hay were easily recognised with its 60-foot high iron chimney *'just beyond the three mile stone from Bath'*. This engine was to prove to be the main source of power in the works for almost thirty years. Steam coal from South Wales, brought to Bath by the Great Western Railway, was used to fire this boiler, while local collieries supplied coal for other boilers. There are many references to the 'Garrett' in the records, its faults, failings and maintenance. Due to the threat of power cuts during the difficult years in the late 1940s, the steam plant was kept as a standby until it was finally replaced in 1948 by an electric motor. A 'donkey' engine with a vertical boiler was used to supply steam to the 24hp winch

RIGHT: Kilns at Combe Hay Works. Kilns No's 3 and 4 were of this type, the other two used steam to dry the earth instead of coke fires. They continued in use for many years until replaced by the louvre dryer in the 1940s.
FROM A SKETCH BY GILBERT HOLLEY

To Winch

Kiln Doors open upwards

Doors into Mill Room

Incline

Earth discharged from Tram

Earth chutes

Removable Kiln Plates with holes at 3/4in centres

Horizontal Girders supporting Kiln Plates

Vertical Iron Columns supporting Girders and bars, to stop lumps of earth or accidents, should a broken plate give way

Coke fire

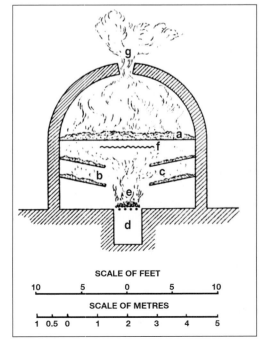

SCALE OF FEET

10   5   0   5   10

SCALE OF METRES

1 0.5 0   1   2   3   4   5

LEFT: Fuller's Earth Kiln. An early example of a fuller's earth kiln appears in Ore and Stone Mining *by C. Le Foster. The first edition appeared in 1894 and the following is based on the 1905 edition. He describes a stationary direct fire kiln as follows:*

'It is a brick or stone building about 36 feet long and 15 feet wide, with an arched roof of brick or a sloping roof of slate. About 9 feet above the bottom is a floor **a**, made of cast iron plates full of holes about 1/8inch in diameter, underneath which are two sets of sloping shelves, made of sheets of iron **b** and **c**, which can be taken out at pleasure; **d** is a deep flue bringing in air from the outside, and having two openings in the kiln, covered with fire bars, upon each of which a coke fire **e**, is maintained. A sheet of corrugated iron **f**, is hung up over each fire, in order to prevent the clay immediately above it from being too strongly heated. Both the upper and lower floors of the kiln can be entered by large doors. The charging is all done from the floor **a**; a few of the plates are taken up on each side, the sheets **b** being removed, and clay is wheeled in barrows along **a** and tipped on to **c**. The plates **b** are replaced and similarly covered with a charge of clay, and finally **a** receives a layer of damp clay 6 to 8 inches thick. The doors are shut and the fires lighted; though the heat is considerable, it is not enough to prevent the men going in from time to time to put on more fuel if required. The moisture-laden air ascends and escapes through the roof at **g**.'

It is possible that the first kilns at Odd Down may have been of this form. We know that when rebuilding did take place in the early 20th century the kilns were of different design.

that pulled the trams up the incline into the kilns when the Garrett was being serviced. The foundry at Bath Tramways supplied rail and tyres for the tramway wagons in 1918 and in the years following.

The other improvements included a new building with walls 18ins thick, which adjoined the old windmill building; the date 1922 has been carved on a stone in the gable end. At the same time, the two Firs Cottages were built, No. 1 being on the Bath side. In the centre of Picket Down stood a small stone powder house, in which blasting powder and detonators were stored at a safe distance from the main workings.

Ore and Stone Mining, published in the early 20th century, described a fuller's earth kiln as being a brick or stone building measuring 36 feet by 15 feet, with an arched roof, and about nine feet above the bottom there was floor on which the earth was dried and turned. A separate source of energy was required for the first stage of refinement, the drying of the wet clods of earth in the kilns. These had been brought from the mine by the trams and discharged into the chutes. A Carey boiler was used for the steam pipes which ran under the plates of No's 1 and 2 kilns on the south west side of the plant. Foundry coke was preferred, or that supplied by the Bath Gas Works, for the fires under kilns No's 3 and 4 to dry the earth to the required level of moisture. In 1920, however, W.H. Keevil wrote from the works at Redhill to his son that colliery coke was too expensive for drying the earth on the kilns and he recommended that they use gas coke from the Radstock Gas Company!

Dobson, the builder from Southstoke, repaired the tiled and vented roofs of No's 2 and 3 kilns in January 1915. He was back in December 1918 to erect columns and girders on firebrick walls in No. 4 kiln, the girders supporting the kiln floors. Early in the following year, this kiln was reconstructed with 73 new perforated, 1in (25mm) thick, iron kiln plates, measuring 2 feet by 1.5 feet (0.6m by 0.46m), with holes $^3/_4$ in (19mm) apart, ordered from Young Brothers of the Walcot Foundry in Bath. Firebricks and clay were obtained from the Cattybrook Brick Co. Ltd at Shortwood near Bristol. A new water supply was piped into the Combe Hay Works at the same time. By September of that year, twenty-six cast-iron columns were needed for No. 3 kiln and a new oil engine was required. In 1920, Dobson was called in to make repairs to the roofs of kilns No's 1, 2 and 3. He had replaced the roof of No. 4 kiln in 1914. It seems that with the installation of the Garrett engine, there was a period of modernisation of plant and equipment.

Two tram tracks ran up two inclines from the mine into the works. The one on the west side was for 'best' earth and therefore called the 'best line'. The other was the 'main line'. Six full trams at a time could be pulled up under the supervision of the winchman. A bell gave warning when to stop the trams. The floor of each tram was then released allowing their combined loads, of between 16 and 20 tons of wet earth, to fall into the chutes below. On each side of the chutes were four heavy iron doors, which were then lifted open, the earth spilled and was shovelled into the kilns alongside. Barrows were used to carry the earth to the farthest parts of the kiln and finally shovelfuls finished off the bed of earth near the doors. The aim of the kilnmen was to spread the earth evenly over the kiln plates and have a layer about 6 inchess (150mm) thick if it was to be dried for one day, and 9 inches (225mm) if two nights were required.

It was essential to have a good fire underneath to dry the earth carefully and in time. The kiln plates had a large number of holes drilled in them, to enable a draught to carry away the moisture through the nine ventilating outlets in the roof. The earth was then broken up and 'turned' after a day and 'fired with ashes' on the second day, *i.e.* using the residual heat in the hot ashes. It was a skilled operation, as care had to be taken to prevent the earth becoming scorched and therefore useless. Experience was the only way to regulate the drying in the kilns. Only ashes were used in the

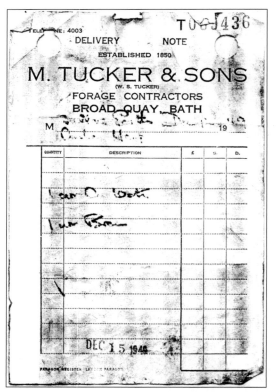

drying of the yellow earth, because coke would have been too hot and 'burnt' the earth, turning it orange-red. This earth was used to make the product known as YB20, required by Boots the Chemists.

There was an art to loading and turning the fuller's earth on the kilns. The firing of a kiln was compared by O. Keevil in 1919 *'to the burning of a hurricane lamp whereby when putting one's hand over the lamp chimney the flame went out instantly. This was analogous to roof ridging, to give increased draughts and freer burning fires the solution was to give more outlet through the roof and floor'*. The same year, when it was known that the lumps were not drying properly on kiln No. 4, W.F. Keevil said that the lumps should be put onto the perforated plates and covered as fully as possible with smaller stuff or they should be broken down between 5am and 7am after being dried overnight. To further reinforce the point, Keevil senior arranged for W. Ironsides, the kiln foreman at Redhill, to come to Combe Hay to show how to use the reconstructed No. 4 kiln. This major reconstruction had required some 3,000 bricks, as well as new columns and girders. Ironsides' instructions were that large lumps were to be broken down and that there had to be plenty of reserve wet earth in the chute. There was to be quick clearance, firing and filling of the kiln. Owen Keevil was to write in 1925, *'after the earth has been dried on the kilns any subsequent contact with water robs it of the qualities which make it an effective refiner of lards and oils'* – in other words, it was then useless.

Fire-bars had to be replaced periodically and the Longmead Foundry in East Twerton supplied them in 1925. Again in May 1937, 228 new ones were ordered for the kilns. The men were reminded that the grates had to be kept free from ash, so as to keep the fire bars cool with a sufficient draught of air. Later in that month, Owen Keevil gave detailed instructions about how to produce specially dried 'All Best' earth, because this could vary with the wind and weather. He pointed out that the kilns generated heat even when the fires had burnt out and that the earth had to be turned very carefully. The ashes from underneath the kilns were taken out through an exit in the south wall. A barrow was used to carry ashes from the kilns and coke furnace over the two railway arches to the dump, in the field to the south west of the works where ash can still be found.

Most of the staff were called for medicals during the First World War but Owen Keevil managed to get conscription deferred. Some men were only fit for home service. Later, fuller's earth workers were exempted from war service but nevertheless some men left to serve. Eventually, in July 1918, the Ministry of National Service recognised the Fullers' Earth Union as government subcontractors and allowed some of the men to be enrolled as War Work Volunteers. The number of employees varied according to the demand for the earth. In April 1921, eleven men were dismissed at Combe Hay and Midford and only nine men were kept on.

In May 1919, during a period of hot weather, the kilnmen Densley and Boddy complained about the amount of heat coming from No. 4 kiln compared to the old steam kilns. They wanted a doorway cut to allow in more air but this was refused by W.F. Keevil because it would be a disadvantage in winter with the cold winds. The problem recurred in May 1933, the men complaining about the heat when turning the earth. This time O. Keevil said that another doorway would affect the performance of the kiln and that Densley was old enough to remember the old kilns when men could only stand

Broad Quay in the 1920s, showing Tucker's warehouses. The one partly hidden on the left was previously occupied by W.H. Coward. Note the travelling fair on the left.
BATH RECORD OFFICE

ten minutes before getting some fresh air! Eventually, some large iron doors were put in.

After drying, the next stage in the refining of the fuller's earth was to prepare it for milling. The Fowler, and later the Garrett, steam engine supplied the power through flax belts to most of the machines that were required for the different processes. The dried lumps of clay from the kilns were shovelled into barrows by the kilnmen and wheeled out into the mill room, where they were tipped into the lump elevator. This consisted of an endless chain of small buckets, which tipped the earth into a chute that fed No. 1 mill. This roller mill was a crusher, or pulveriser, which smashed up the lumps of earth sufficiently to allow the coarse powder to be passed on to the powder elevator. This in turn fed the dresser, a sieving machine, which used screens of silk bolting cloth of different mesh size, to produce the level of fineness that each customer required.

The Newago Separator, which originally had been supplied to H.N. Garrett Ltd at Midford in 1913-14, was moved to Combe Hay and installed there in 1921. It was used to extract all the coarse material from the dried and crushed earth as it left the mill, as this would have cut the fine silk bolting cloths of the dresser. It was therefore a preliminary sifter and extracted all material from the mill of 30-mesh and upwards. It then carried the earth to the top of the building, for its journey down through the various stages of refining. The dresser would eventually finish the powder to approximately 200-mesh fineness. Other belts and pulleys led off the engine to the blender and the mill which produced the final fine powder. The mixing or sifting machines, made by Ransome & Rapier Ltd of Ipswich and the Sturtevant Engineering Co. Ltd of Aylesbury, were required to blend

Right: Combe Hay Fuller's Earth Works as shown on the 25ins OS 1932 edition map. This arrangement of buildings probably remained the same until the extensions during the Second World War. The tramways have been modified with a new adit and loading bay near Combe Hay lane, as extraction was now from the north side of the Fosse Way. The reservoir has also been enlarged.

Below: Notepaper of the Fullers' Earth Union, Limited. Note the Company's trademark and the awards gained at various exhibitions from 1851. The head office at 4 Cullum Street, London EC3, was destroyed in WWII and thereafter moved to the works at Redhill. FULLER'S EARTH ARCHIVES AT THE MUSEUM OF BATH AT WORK

the various mixtures of fuller's earth with other compounds, such as china clay and soda ash which different customers required. W.F. Keevil, writing to his son in 1919, hoped that when the new Garrett engine was installed it would be easier to get the earth to run down the various chutes and silks that dressed it. He thought the increased power and vibration might prevent the powder from 'hanging'. The degree of moisture in the dried earth was critical, as if it was still too damp it could cause the silk sheets in the dresser to burst with consequent loss of production.

In September 1919, if all was going well at the Combe Hay Works, they were able to produce 3.5 tons of milled fuller's earth per hour as well as 'best yellow lump'. By 1921, 200 tons of ground fuller's earth per week were required by customers. In September 1922, the boiler was de-scaled and the plant given a thorough overhaul. It seems that by this time they were able to produce 10 tons of powdered earth each day. There was the problem at that time of dust in the mill room, which resulted in two tons of fine powder being lost, so a partition was erected. Much later, there was a proper dust extraction plant but the first dust collecting machinery was installed in 1927. Among the documents there is a sketch of dust collector silos, of which there were

twelve, which used baffles to trap the fine powder suspended in the air. These were possibly installed in Owen Keevil's day. This powder was recovered from the silos, rather than being wasted.

In March 1925 Owen Keevil received a letter from Erdwerke München, a German Fuller's Earth Company, in which an Otto Lietzenmayer stated that, when Bavarian earth was treated chemically, it was five times more efficient for fade than English earth. Owen took this to mean its bleaching power. Otto also stated that oil manufacturers were always asking for more of this prepared earth and that he was prepared to investigate the chemical treatment of English earth if he was sent samples. In a letter to his father regarding this matter, Owen comments *'Now we know that German chemists are very good chemists and I suggest that we should not lose anything by sending him samples. Upon the other hand, it is just possible we may gain something. If we could get him to send us back his treated samples for testing ourselves we may find out what he does to it and in case we may learn something by listening to what he has to say. I suggest that we send him some Somerset earth for experiment and ask him to let us have back for test any improved earth which he obtains from it.'* This would have been the start of the development of treating earth with soda ash at Bath and with hydrochloric acid at Redhill.

During the 1930s, further improvements took place. The two Keevils patented their own elevator mixer machine in 1932 and claimed *'it is quite the finest dry mixing machine on the market'*. They were prepared to demonstrate it to any interested parties. This period saw the introduction of more internal combustion power plants in the form of Petter engines. In December 1938, an automatic lighting system powered by a Petter diesel engine was installed in the kiln chamber, many years after Owen Keevil had asked for electrical lighting. The same engine also drove the blender in the mill room. This remained in use until the works were connected to mains electricity in November 1942. Under the Factory Act of 1938, a proper dust extraction plant had to be installed and this was finally in place by September 1940.

In May 1938, Admiral Butler and his wife visited Combe Hay Works. He was a shareholder of the company, and a nephew of the Butler who had built the works and been one of the founders of the Somerset fuller's earth industry at the end of the previous century.

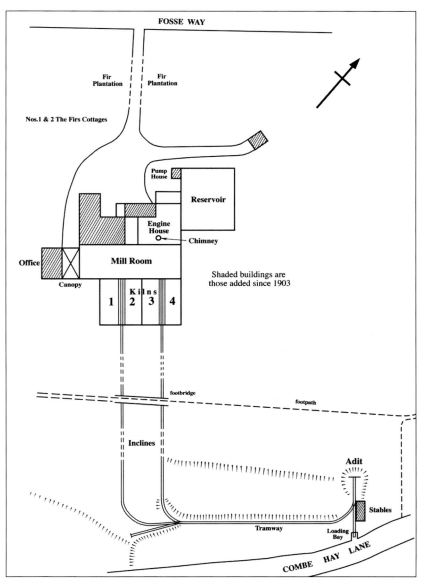

Plan of the Combe Hay Fuller's Earth Works, c.1932. Buildings added since the 1903 map are shown shaded.

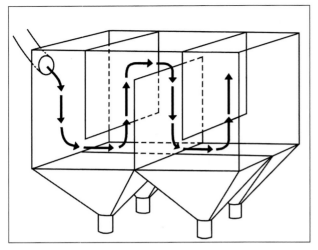

Early Dust Plant. This sketch may have been an early attempt at a dust extraction plant or to obtain different mesh sizes of the dried and milled fuller's earth. Dust was always a problem for the workers until eventually an efficient extraction plant was installed. A note at the bottom of the sketch reads 'Am afraid the 'perspective' is somewhat awry!, but hope the above will give you Mr. W.F.K.'s idea of baffles'. Presumably someone at Redhill was suggesting what might be tried at Combe Hay.
FULLER'S EARTH ARCHIVES AT THE MUSEUM OF BATH AT WORK

NOTES TO CHAPTER 6

In 1905, **C. Le Neve Foster** commented that fuller's earth has to be **dressed** before marketing, therefore it is dried, sifted and ground. It is sifted by hand to take out the fine, if the customer insists on having nothing but lumps. Dry lumps are put into sacks and the small is sifted again. The very fine, below $1/8$ inch, is thrown away and the coarser part is ground to a fine flour in a mill and so sold. In addition to dry dressing, some of the clay is ground in an edge-runner, run into settling tanks and dried in much the same way as china clay.

Michael Yates, who worked at Redhill, has pointed out that in the late 1890s or early 20th century Johnson 'Dragon' mills of the ring roller type were installed and continued in use in the fuller's earth industry at both Redhill and Combe Hay for many years. This sheds light on the quotation in the Fullers' Earth Union Ltd *Prospectus* of 23rd March 1890, referring to Combe Hay:

'The Machinery with which the Works are fitted is of modern type, and the arrangements for canal and railway carriage are excellent, but the demands of the American trade have been so heavy that others have had to be not only delayed but refused, because the drying and grinding plant has been inadequate. The application of a small part of the working Capital of £10,000 will enable the Directors to meet the exigencies of this rapidly-increasing and profitable trade … by at once providing more drying stoves. The grinding plant has, in view of this development, been largely increased within the last few months, and the new machinery is included in the purchase.'

C.L. Parsons, an American chemist, was to write in 1907:

'American vs. English Fuller's Earth. Although America furnishes all of the fuller's earth used on petroleum, it supplies but a small portion of that used on edible oils, the English earth being considered superior to any American earth yet marketed for this purpose. For a fuller's earth to supplant the English earth in American practice, it must have the following properties, given in the order of their importance: (1) It must bleach as well as the English; (2) It must not cause the color of the oil to revert; (3) It must filter well; (4) It must absorb no more oil than the English; (5) It must not catch fire when removed from the presses; (6) It must give no permanent taste or odor … Most American earths do not bleach as well as the English.'

THE EARLIER METHOD OF PROCESSING FULLER'S EARTH AT COMBE HAY WORKS

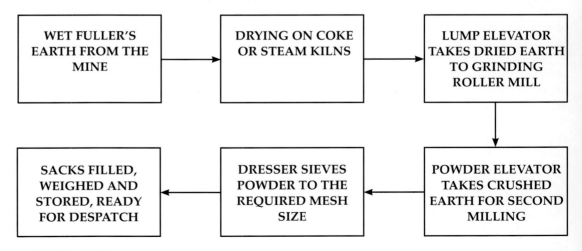

BIBLIOGRAPHY

Doughty, Martin, & Ward, Owen, 'Shortwood Brickworks', *Bristol Industrial Archaeological Society Journal*, No. 8, 1975
Foster, C. Le Neve, *Ore and Stone Mining*, 1905
Parsons, C.L., article on fuller's earth in *The American Chemical Society Journal*, Apr. 1907, reprinted in *The Mineral Industry*, 1907 ed., USA

Chapter 7

WINNING AND WORKING THE EARTH

The Conditions Underground

Winning the fuller's earth on Odd Down, was no easy task. The hours were long, often in damp, cramped conditions. As with the processing of the fuller's earth, where there were changes and development, things also changed underground. Modern methods were gradually introduced to overcome some of the problems that were encountered underground over the years.

VENTILATION

For years, the only form of ventilation was the draught produced by air entering the adits and escaping through the large number of vertical shafts dug for this purpose. At least five such vents were dug on Picket Down, as this area was extensively mined in the early years of the 20th century.

The air in the underground workings was often very bad, especially during periods of thundery weather. Sometimes the miners were moved elsewhere to work in areas near the airshafts. During 1928, the miners had been forced to get earth by irregular working on eighty days due to bad air and it was agreed that some form of mechanical ventilation was urgently required before the following summer. The first attempt to improve the supply of fresh air was by using a Petter diesel engine, to pump air into the workings through a small pipe in December 1937! This was eventually replaced by electrically driven fans, which created a good supply of air underground.

Further airshafts were dug from time to time, as the workings extended ever more widely from the original galleries. These shafts were over 50 feet (15m) deep and took some time to dig through the hard overlying rock before being lined with wood. A rope ladder hanging in an airshaft provided an escape route in an emergency. Later, a wooden ladder was put in one of the shafts. The extension of the galleries also required hard digging and the use of explosives to get through faults to expose good seams of earth. On one occasion, 18 inches (0.45m) of 'bungum', *i.e.* waste material, had to be removed to give the men enough headroom in which to work.

The airshafts were a source of danger and in 1934, the wire fencing at the surface was replaced with square mesh sheep netting. There was a fatal accident involving a local boy, who fell down the No. 5 airshaft in the summer of 1948, and although the fence and planks protecting the shaft had been in place before the accident, the company were forced to carry out more safety precautions. There was also the problem of vandals and a gate was fitted across the main entrance to the mine in 1940.

In the autumn of 1948, the manager, Tom Holmes, wanted another airshaft; the law stated that they were to be placed every 220 yards (200m) on a straight underground road. Electrical ventilation was due to be installed and a new shaft was agreed by the management. When the electrical fan started in May of the next year, it produced a very good draught and could be left to run overnight. The fan house was on the surface with ducts into the underground workings. Another new shaft was

Abandonment Plans. This plan only shows the extent of the underground excavations south of the Fosse Way and Combe Hay Lane, and towards the Burnt House public house. The entrance to the last mine, the Grove, was at the southern edge of this plan. FROM A SITE INVESTIGATION REPORT & STRUCTURAL SURVEY OF ABANDONED FULLER'S EARTH WORKS, ODD DOWN, BATH. GCP ARCHITECTS, AUGUST 2002

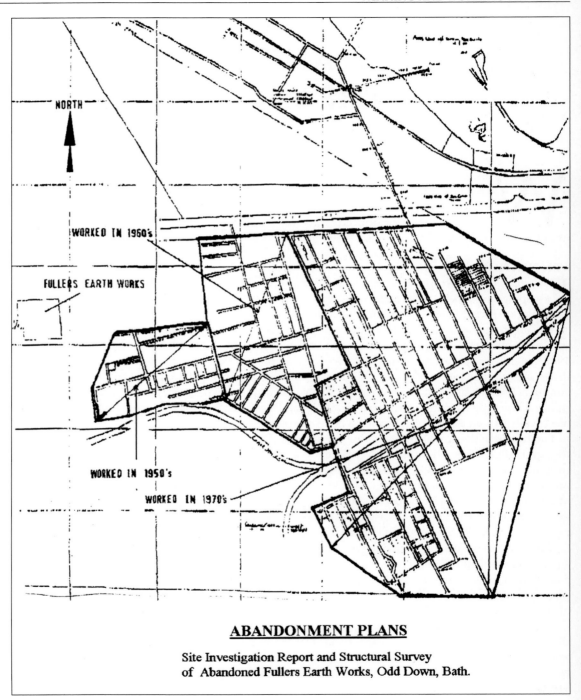

NORTH

WORKED IN 1960's

FULLERS EARTH WORKS

WORKED IN 1950's

WORKED IN 1970's

ABANDONMENT PLANS

Site Investigation Report and Structural Survey
of Abandoned Fullers Earth Works, Odd Down, Bath.

required in the East Drift in 1951 and this was probably some 55 feet (17m) deep. It was the third shaft in the area.

WATER

Flooding was a recurring problem underground. In January 1919, it occurred after a rapid thaw when the pumps could not cope with the large volume of water. The correspondence records that *'over a mile of main pony roads were ruined by an influx of water'*. There was more flooding the following month. In January of the next year, the pit was again flooded due to excessive rainfall and a quarter of the work force was off sick. The workings often became wet after periods of rain, as the water soaked through the overlying Oolite, leaving the galleries ankle-deep in water.

Drains were cut in the workings to make them self-draining but it was not completely successful. In periods of heavy rain, serious flooding could cause the complete cessation of mining until the water subsided. Water also came into the mine from joints in the seams of rock below the fuller's earth, as well as down the airshafts and from underground springs in Vernham Wood. The workings towards Dunkerton on the west side of the Fosse Way, known to the miners as the 'Clapham Junction Drift', were particularly susceptible to flooding from water coming down an airshaft and through the roof, with the added danger of the roof collapsing into the roadways. The underground roads sloped downwards from the entrance near the plant, towards the Clapham Junction Drift and therefore this continued to be a particularly wet area of the mine. In June 1948, the East Drift, also to the west of the Fosse Way but towards the Burnt House Inn, was flooded and had to be cleared by hand pump.

The problem of flooding continued. In December 1948, the water was 4 feet (1.2m) deep in places and this time the Englishcombe side remained dry while the Combe Hay side was flooded. It was possible that the water had drained into the large area which had been worked out. In February of the following year, there was flooding despite thirty hours of pumping. Between thirty and forty tram loads of earth collapsed in the East Drift. The disruptions due to flooding meant that mining was held up until the workings had been pumped out.

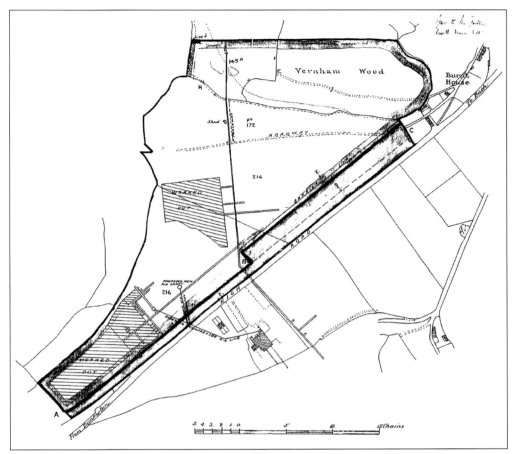

Copy of the old 1884 map with modern buildings and the extensive excavations in the Duchy. The 'Clapham Junction Drift' was at the south western end and the 'East Drift' was towards Burnt House.
GCP ARCHITECTS, AUGUST 2002

ROCK FALLS AND SUBSIDENCE

The work was dangerous and rock falls could occur at any time. Falls of the overlying rock also caused blockages in the tramways. There was a particularly serious one in October 1924, which brought all mining to a halt for a whole week. On another occasion, a substantial roof fall on the new Vernham Wood adit meant that one of the main underground roads had to be driven round the blockage, so that earth could still be won.

After an area had been 'worked out', the ground above tended to subside, the timber props collapsing under the strain of the rock above and the overlying surface showed a series of depressions. Subsidence usually occurred within three months, with more over the following years in the older workings. In general, the extraction of the earth did not cause difficulties in the use of the land above for agricultural purposes. In the late 1960s and early 1970s, builders' rubble was tipped on much of the site to restore ground levels.

MINERS' SAFETY

During the First World War, applications were made to the Ministry of Munitions of War for exemptions to allow 3lbs (1.4kg) of carbide per week for use in miners' lamps. The state of the flame in the lamp gave an indication of the quality of the air in the mine. Charlie Swatton has pointed out that, in fact, the carbide lamps, which burnt acetylene, did not give a good warning of bad air and so a tallow candle was always kept burning near where the men were working. If its flame started to die, it indicated that the level of oxygen was poor and the workings should be evacuated until the air cleared. When the miners spoke of the air being bad, it probably meant that there was a higher level of carbon dioxide present. The dangerous firedamp found in coal mines seldom occurred in the fuller's earth workings.

At times, the miners had to be reminded of the safety regulations, and they had to work within sight and sound of each other in case there was a fall of earth. The major cause of accidents underground was from roof falls and eventually steel helmets were issued to the miners. Jim Woolman, who worked in the industry in the 1950s for a short time, remembered that, when underground, if the miners saw a trickle of clay coming from the roof, they left quickly as this was a sign of a possible roof fall; some six of these could occur in a week. The main health hazards were lumbago and injuries to the back. There was also the danger of runaway trams and accidents involving the cable and winch which hauled the trams into the works. Nicholds was in favour of good relations with the unions and in October 1948, most of the men joined the Municipal & General Workers Union. From the evidence that survives, it appears that there were no very serious accidents at Combe Hay or the Duchy and that most injuries occurred above ground.

TRAMWAYS

As the area of mining extended, it meant that the working faces were at a considerable distance from the processing plant. The miners demanded higher wages for having to push the trams over 120 yards (110m) and these were paid. There was a considerable descent in gradient at the Clapham Junction Drift near the top of Dunkerton Hill.

In some places, concrete was laid between the sleepers of the tramways, presumably to give a better grip to the ponies hauling the trams. By June 1945, Holmes was requesting the use of underground turntables to reduce the amount of manhandling of the trams. These turntables were made, together with the rails and trams, by Bolling & Love. The wheels of the trams were cast by

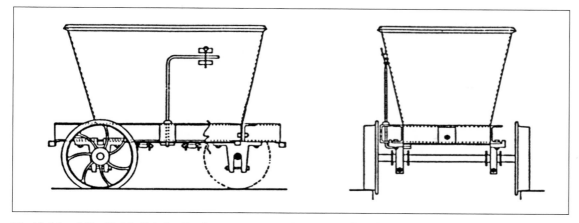

Left: Drawing of a 2ft 7.5in. gauge wagon. These were used before they were replaced by more modern 2ft gauge wagons. Wheels cast by Hadfields Ltd of Sheffield.
BRIAN CLARKE

Below: The Eimco RockerShovel Loader. Made by Eimco Mining Machinery, Envirotech Corporation, Salt Lake City, Utah, USA.
EIMCO MINING MACHINERY, ENVIROTECH CORPORATION TECHNICAL BROCHURE

Hadfields of Sheffield. Originally the gauge was 2 foot $7^1/_2$ inches (0.8m), before it was changed to the more modern 2 foot (0.6m). For a period it is possible that there was dual gauge track in some parts of the mine. The mechanical 'Eimco' shovels, used underground in later years to load the mine cars after the earth had been drilled from the seam with pneumatic picks, were mounted on small flanged wheels and looked like hunched stag beetles!

John Church and Ray Ashman, Mines Inspectors, were called in during the last period of mining as there was some concern about the safety of the galleries which ran under Combe Hay Lane. There was a very long tunnel from No. 3 adit which went under the lane and the Fosse Way. It then crossed the geological fault, which ran in a direction from north west to south east, where there was a drop of some 33 feet (10m).

In the final years of working, the main haulage galleries were supported by semicircular steel arches and beneath the public roads they were further reinforced with concrete. Between the steel arches, the walls of the gallery were sometimes lined with the steel mesh used in concrete work. To ensure support for the Fosse Way, a strip of ground was left unworked on either side of this road and there was a similar restriction on Kilkenny Lane.

Illness and age among the ponies led to discussion on replacing them with a battery powered electric locomotive. Owen Keevil had wanted to introduce electric or steam locomotives as far back as 1929 but nothing came of it. It had to be the smallest locomotive made. Matters came

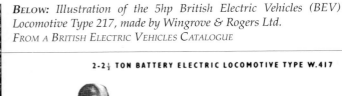

ABOVE: *The electric battery locomotive pulling a train of trams out of the adit near the Combe Hay works in the early 1950s.* SOMERSET COUNTRYMAN, VOL. 17

BELOW: *The locomotive along with six mine cars at the Grove mine during the severe winter of 1962-63.* BERT UPSHALL COLLECTION

to a head when all three ponies escaped from the field where they had been left over the Whit holiday long weekend. The works were closed for an outing on the Whit Tuesday and the loss was not discovered until the next day. They had to be retrieved from Shoscombe, several miles away, by two employees, Bert Upshall and Stan Love!

The company took delivery on 3rd May 1948 of a 5hp British Electric Vehicles (BEV) Locomotive Type 217, made by Wingrove & Rogers Ltd. A long wait followed, as this required heavier rails of 16lbs/ft (23.8kg/m). There was also a delay while a battery charging shed was built on the west side of the former stables. These stables were located on the north side of Combe Hay Lane, set into the bank to the right of the entrance to an adit. The three stalls for the ponies were built of local stone and roofed with red tiles, with a loft for the storage of fodder. The new shed was built of red bricks with a corrugated asbestos roof, and it also provided a place to recharge the electric lamps now worn on the helmets of the underground workers. These had replaced the carbide lamps used for so many years.

The result was that this locomotive was not

finally commissioned until 11th June 1949. Initially it was unable to haul six trams, each with a payload of 12cwt (610kg), if the wheels slipped on greasy rails, unless sand was used to prevent this. Some of the ponies had been able to pull that number of trams! However, it was the end of the era for the ponies. It was decided to sell 'Tom', pension off 'Prince', who had been bought for £42 in 1921, and retain 'Sandy'. 'Podger', bought in 1933, was over twenty-seven years old and retired by this time, along with Bert Upshall's pony 'Nobby'.

LEFT: 'Nobby', the pony that Bert Upshall worked with, enjoying the sunshine in the field beside the works.
BERT UPSHALL COLLECTION

BELOW: A visit by the Mayor on 17th September 1952. The manager Mr Tom Holmes, is in the centre, with Mr. R. Nicholds from the Redhill works and the Mayor, Alderman A.W.S. Berry, to his right. A 'mucking tram' or cart, made at the works for waste from the mine, is in the foreground and the men on the right are holding the carbide lamps then in use underground. A miner, George Legg, and a journalist are in the background.
BATH & WILTS CHRONICLE

PRODUCTION

Jim Woolman worked underground and in the milling room in the early 1950s. He described the mining as being very hard, working a 40-hour week with only a twenty-minute break each day. Some men only lasted a few days as a miner in the days after the Second World War, before asking if there were other jobs available. Work was from 6am until 5pm, including overtime. Some miners were on piece-work while others were paid on an hourly basis with take home pay around £70.

Between four and six men would be working underground. The miners usually dug and loaded sixteen tram loads per day but this rose to eighteen loads during the Second World War and in 1946, due to high demand, it was expected that this might have to be increased to twenty loads. On some occasions, depending on demand, three shifts were worked. Six steel side-tipping trams were used for taking out the waste, which were known as 'mucking trams'.

After the digging, the next job was to put up the timber props and then go out and get more for the next day's work. This could take up to four hours. The timber was stacked near the factory, where it was cut to size before a horse and chain dragged the props down to the tramway. There they were loaded onto a tram and taken underground. After being fitted, some of the pit props would break during the night and have to be replaced when the workings were checked the following morning.

Owen Keevil had once forecast a yield of 10,000 tons per acre (24,710 tons/ha). The Fullers' Earth Union owned a total of 36 acres (14.5ha) but 4 acres (1.6ha) had to be deducted for faults. Further exploration for

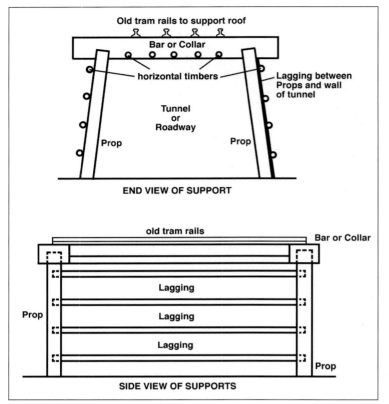

END VIEW OF SUPPORT

Old tram rails to support roof

Bar or Collar

horizontal timbers

Lagging between
Props and wall
of tunnel

Tunnel
or
Roadway

Prop   Prop

old tram rails

Bar or Collar

Lagging

Lagging

Lagging

Prop   Prop

SIDE VIEW OF SUPPORTS

Diagram showing the roof support of the galleries. Timber props supported the bar or collar, and timber fitted between the props and the walls was known as lagging. Old rails were used to support the roof and later removed.

FROM A SKETCH BY BERT UPSHALL

good seams of earth were carried out in May 1943, when new bore holes were sunk in the vicinity of Sulis Manor at South Stoke, on Mr G.W. Hignett's land, and at Grove Wood, to the east of the old Combe Hay Lower Works. In 1949, the management at Redhill wanted samples from every foot, after the first 20 feet (6m), in trial bore holes with a rotary drill in the area of Sulis Manor. The owner, Mr Souster, said that when a well was sunk on his property, fuller's earth was found at 69 feet (23m) and solid rock at 100 feet (30m). The best yellow earth came from the 'Duchy', the area to the west of the Fosse Way, in the parish of Englishcombe. Combe Hay only produced green earth, which was blue-grey in colour and less soapy to the touch.

MINING BY THE PILLAR AND STALL METHOD

For most of the time that fuller's earth was mined in this area, the pillar and stall method of extraction was used, as in local stone and coalmines. The pillars of rock and clay which were left to support the limestone roof between the roadways, were approximately 49 feet (15m) square and therefore some 25% of the usable earth was left behind. Extraction took place at a depth of about 59-82 feet (18-25m) below ground level, access being gained, for many years, via adits that were driven into the hillside to the west of Combe Hay lane. In the East Drift, the gradient was downhill towards Odd Down and in some places the seams there were 7 feet (2.1m), so the men stood on tins to reach the highest parts!

The galleries at right angles to the main roadway were supported with 'sets', *i.e.* two vertical pine timbers 12 inches (300mm) in diameter, notched into a horizontal piece across the top known as a 'bar' or 'collar'. Horizontal timbers, 4 inches (100mm) in diameter, were fitted between each set and these were known as 'leggings', possibly a corruption of lagging. The Longleat Estate supplied some of the timber for the props. The roof between the props was also supported with old rails, which would be removed later.

While the earth was being dug out between two parallel galleries, the roof was supported temporarily with 6 inch (150mm) diameter props wedged against the roof. When the timber roof supports gave way and possibly some of the pillars of fuller's earth that had been left, under the weight of the overburden, it caused the roof to collapse and eventually subsidence was visible on the surface.

Throughout the period of mining little spoil was brought to the surface, as most of it was put back into the workings. The excavation of the seam was only 5-6 feet (1.5-1.8m) deep, occasionally up to 7 feet (2.1m). Approximately once a quarter, the side-tipping trams were loaded with spoil and discharged to the south west of the works on a spur track of the tramway. The area later became extensively covered with brambles.

Rails from the Horsecombe Vale incline were brought over in September 1948 for use in the new

East Drift road. This proved to be a good source of fuller's earth, with the seam up to 9 feet (2.7m) in depth and where the alkalinity of the earth was lower at the top of the seam than in the middle. At the end of 1948, Tom Holmes introduced a 'Ski-Hi' hydraulic jack. This was to be used to support the roof when sets were replaced and was also used for robbing out, that is excavating the extremities where the sets were too low to allow a tram to pass. The following year a second jack was ordered.

It was not until the late 1940s that more modern methods of mining were being considered, instead of the pick and shovel which had been used since mining had started. A pneumatic 'clay digger', namely a ripping pick, was considered in August 1946 but it weighed 23lbs (10kg). Climax Rock Drills had sent details of their pneumatic picks and clay diggers. Owen Keevil had investigated pneumatic picks and spades as far back as May 1929 but may have decided against their use then as it would have required constant ventilation. It was believed that modern tools would increase production by 25% and this could result in the loss of a miner. Trials were carried out in the autumn of 1946 with the clay digger, a spade with a small blade. The compressor for the air was situated on the surface near the fan house above the East Drift. The introduction of electric lighting underground was discussed in July 1947 as an improvement to working conditions and this was eventually installed.

Cloth map showing all the underground workings, except the very early work on the south side of Fosse Way. Drawn on the 1903 OS map.
BATH ROYAL LITERARY & SCIENTIFIC INSTITUTION

MINING BY THE RETREAT METHOD

The Avon County Council Report, *Mineral Working in Avon* 1978, described the last method of extraction used at the mine:

'Until recently all clay was extracted by the pillar and stall method, but a different and more modern method of working is now used in one part of the mine. This employs large hydraulic jacks to support the roof while extraction of the 3m (10ft) thick seam of clay takes place beneath the jack canopy. Work is begun at the furthest part of the mine and progresses back towards the entrance – hence the term 'retreat mining'. When the jacks are withdrawn the roof collapses almost immediately. This method is extremely efficient because total extraction of the clay is possible and the immediate initiation of settlement after

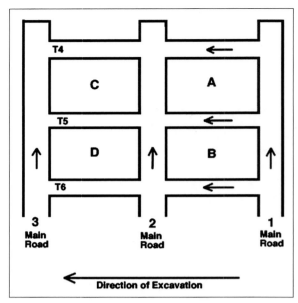

ABOVE: Diagram to illustrate 'Robbing'. Up to three parallel tunnels were driven to the end of the ground to be worked and these were connected by transverse tunnels. The roof would be supported while area 'A', followed by area 'B', was worked out. Afterwards, the timber props were removed and the roof allowed to collapse. The miners would then move on to areas 'C' and 'D'.
FROM A SKETCH BY BERT UPSHALL

jack removal promotes the early stabilisation of the ground. Additional roof support is provided by the timber props on the roadways and also by a thin limestone bed which is left in situ above the seam. A further 15m (24ft) is left unworked on either side of the Fosse Way and the small lane which passes over the workings in order to ensure their stability. The adits are also lined with concrete where they pass under the Fosse Way.'

These steel chocks, made by Fletcher, Sutcliffe Wild, consisted of three huge 12 inch (305mm) diameter hydraulic props, supporting a steel canopy under which the miners worked. The chocks, each weighing 4.5 tons, could 'walk' forwards or backwards under the power of a horizontal hydraulic ram and they were able to exert an initial pressure of 1250lbs per sq.in (87.5kg/sq.cm) on the roof. This pressure was provided by an electric hydraulic pump situated outside the adit. They were installed around 1974 at a cost of £36,000. The hydraulic supports could be used repeatedly and they helped to boost output by up to 12%, so that at that stage the weekly production was in the order of 800 tons. The use of wooden props was therefore unnecessary in the later workings and a larger amount of earth could be extracted.

The plateau outside the new Grove Mine c1968, looking west. In the background is a pile of timber for lagging the areas to be mined. The steel girders in the foreground were for supporting the main galleries. The shelter on the left covered the concrete bins into which the earth from the mine was tipped.
GORDON & PATRICK HIGGS, GLOUCESTERSHIRE SOCIETY FOR INDUSTRIAL ARCHAEOLOGY

In the final years, the last workings at Combe Hay were referred to as the 'Grove' or the 'Southstoke Mine', as they were within that parish. To the east of Combe Hay Lane there were three adits which emerged onto a small plateau. The adits split the area to be worked into 300 foot (91m) blocks. No. 1 adit, to the south, was driven out from the internal workings. It was near here that the old Combe Hay Lower Works had produced yellow earth at the end of the 19th century. Gilbert Holley was among those who had filled in the old stone-lined airshaft. Later, the last manager would not accept that this area had been worked out many years before when Gilbert's grandfather had been a miner there. In consequence, when work started on the No. 1 adit, they came across the old workings!

Adits No's 2 and 3 were driven inwards and the entrance to No. 3 was concreted. This tunnel was reinforced with steel arches for the first 100 yards (91m), and then timbers and board lining were used for the rest of the workings. The No. 3 adit was started in May 1968, as was the new tunnel at the Duchy. It was the manager, Horace Beech, who had come from the coal industry, who introduced the semicircular steel arches or 'irons' to support the main roadways. From these ran timber-supported roads, with working taking place at two to four faces. The miners did not think that the steel arches were as good as the timber supports for the tunnel roof. A new fan house for No. 3 adit was in use by August 1968 and that for No. 2 adit was still in use at this time. This adit, along with No. 1 adit, was blocked off and only used for ventilation. The remains of a substantial Roman settlement were discovered when widening the No. 3 adit, as mentioned previously. The findings included three stone coffins.

These last workings were exploited from May 1968, until the industry closed for economic reasons in 1980, even though it had

Above: Miner Eric Collins uses a pneumatic pick at the face of a thick seam of 'blue' fuller's earth.
Gordon & Patrick Higgs, Gloucestershire Society for Industrial Archaeology

Left: The Grove Mine. The substantial entrance to Adit No. 3, where the last mining took place from 1968 until the close in 1980, with miners Eric Collins and Brian Rabbits. Only the first 100 yards of the tunnel were steel-reinforced and then it was timbered.
Mrs E. Holmes collection

ABOVE: Inside the new adit showing the arches, the ventilation ducting and pipeline for the pneumatic picks. Note also the wet conditions under foot and the rails leading off into other galleries.

ABOVE RIGHT: The first few yards of the new adit were supported by semicircular steel arches and corrugated iron.

RIGHT: The entrance to the new adit in 1968. Note the ducting carrying fresh air into the mine.
ALL GORDON & PATRICK HIGGS GLOUCESTERSHIRE SOCIETY FOR INDUSTRIAL ARCHAEOLOGY

been estimated that there were deposits for another eight years. When driving in the adits at this last site, the miners eventually hit the geological fault, with a difference in the levels in the seam of 33 feet (10m) in just over 60 yards (55m). To overcome this 1-in-5 gradient, the old electric winch from the works was used to pull the trams up the slope in No. 3 adit. They were then able to extract the earth which it had been impossible to reach when the Vernham Wood venture failed in the early 1960s.

The roof cover was 60-80 feet (18-24m) of Oolite limestone and the depth of the seam between 8-10.5 feet (2.4-3.2m). Having been dug, the clay was loaded manually into the side-tipping 'Rugga' mining cars. At the working face it was separated, into 'top seam', the top 1-3 feet (0.3-0.9m) which contained the most impurities – such as roof rock impurities – whilst the bulk was the purer 'whole seam'. After all the roads in a particular section had been driven and worked, the 16.5 yard (15m) pillars could be partially removed, thus reducing the amount of the mineral which was left behind.

A clear illustration of how the timber lagging was erected. Two miners are showing members of the GSIA round the mine in 1968. Compare the side-tipping mine-cart with the diagram on page 85.
GORDON & PATRICK HIGGS, GLOUCESTERSHIRE SOCIETY FOR INDUSTRIAL ARCHAEOLOGY

In September 1978, the manager, Horace Beech, described the current scene in a short paper:

> *'The Mine at present employs 25 workmen of which 14 are engaged in actual extraction work using pneumatic picks powered by outbye compressors, and hand loading into the mine cars which have a payload of 12cwt [610kg], these being marshalled and brought out of the mine using a small battery locomotive. The gradient is not excessive, approximately one in sixty in favour of the loads. The mine cars are side-tipping and the earth is stored in a 300 ton loading bay for transport to the Works. To ease the burden of hand loading, two 'Eimco' Loading Shovels [RockerShovel Loader] are used when conditions allow. The lorry is loaded from the loading bay by a Massey Ferguson Shovel, and a standby shovel and lorry are kept in service.'*

Ed Croker's last job, in the final days, was to tip the earth from No. 3 adit, still separated into whole seam and top seam, into the three concrete bins. Dave Smart may have been responsible for the maintenance of all the electrical equipment at the mine. The earth was then transported along the old Combe Hay track, which had been metalled between the mine and Combe Hay Lane, and thence via the Lane and the Fosse Way to the plant, where it was stored until required for processing. On the plateau, there was a hut built of breeze blocks where the battery locomotive was recharged and an ex-army wooden hut, which was used as a storeroom and as an office for Frank Cox, the mine foreman. Later it was used as a mess room by the men.

Further into the main galleries of the mine the semicircular steel arches were replaced with vertical and horizontal steel girders. Note the boulders of rock behind the steel mesh lagging.
GORDON & PATRICK HIGGS, GLOUCESTERSHIRE SOCIETY FOR INDUSTRIAL ARCHAEOLOGY

The Avon Report described the situation after mining:

> *'A major consequence of the mining operations is the subsidence of the land surface which takes place following the*

collapse of the workings. Initial collapse, unless induced by retreat mining, takes place after a few weeks when the pillars which have been robbed give way. The timber-supported roofs tend to collapse after 1-2 years and there is also the possibility of further subsidence after 5-7 years due to the final rotting and failure of the wooden supports.

On the surface the land sinks by 1-2 metres [3.2-6.5ft] in a fairly regular plane. Much of the land has been restored to agricultural use by stripping off the topsoil, bringing the surface up to the original level by tipping and then covering the area with new topsoil. It has been claimed that the restored land allows better and earlier crop development due to improved drainage and the quality of the topsoil.'

With retreat mining, the subsidence was quickly induced by the periodic removal of the jacks. Signs of subsidence were evident before the present Park & Ride site was built and can still be seen in the field to the east of Combe Hay Lane, called Sowhills.

Most of the land to the west of the Fosse Way and some to the east had been filled and restored before the end of the industry, while a large area has been reclaimed during the 1990s for the Odd Down Park & Ride site, between the Fosse Way and Combe Hay Lane.

NOTES TO CHAPTER 7

'**The Duchy**' – the name used by the miners for all Duchy of Cornwall land in which the Company had been granted mining rights by the Duchy Estate. This lay within the parish of Englishcombe.

Some **common terms** used in the mining of fuller's earth:

Adit	The horizontal opening or passage into a mine
Drift	A horizontal or oblique underground excavation or passage
Gallery	An underground roadway
Heading	A small passage to be enlarged into a tunnel
Road	An underground passage
Robbing	The digging out of the mineral in difficult areas of the mine
Shaft	A vertical passage for ventilation and possible emergency evacuation
Spoil	The waste, the unwanted material from the mine
Tram	A mine car, tub or skip for carrying the mineral
Turntable	A steel plate for rotating a single tram
Winning	The opening up of a new portion of a seam containing the mineral
Working	The excavating of the required mineral

The **locomotive** made by Wingrove & Rogers Ltd of Liverpool weighed between 2 and 2.5 tons and was 5hp. It was able to pull 16 tons on level track and at the time of purchase, together with the battery charger, cost over £2,000.

The **RockerShovel Loader** was made by Eimco Mining Machinery, Envirotech Corporation, Salt Lake City, Utah, USA

BIBLIOGRAPHY

Avon County Council Report *Mineral Working in Avon 1978*

Brown, C.J., 'A Geotechnical study of abandoned mineworkings in the Bath area'. Unpublished thesis, University of Bristol, 1991

Crocker, Horace, 'How I sampled a mud sandwich with mine hosts', *Bath Chronicle*, 22nd June 1979

Hale, Philip. M., His evidence to the Public Inquiry: *Land at Odd Down, near Bath. Appeal by Bath City Council*, February 1989

Moorlock, B.S.P. & Highley, D.E., *An Appraisal of Fuller's Earth Resources in England and Wales*, British Geological Survey Technical Report WA/91/75, 1991

Price, Rosalind & Watts, Lorna, 'Rescue Excavations at Combe Hay 1968-73', *Somerset Archaeology & Natural History Society Proceedings*, Vol. 124, 1980

Williams, A.E., 'Fuller's Earth. Some notes on its mining, preparation and properties', *The Mining Journal*, 1948

Wyatt, R.J. & Merriman, R.J., 'The Fuller's Earth Deposits at Combe Hay, near Bath', *Guide for Field Excursion E5 International Clay Conference*, 1978

❧ Chapter 8 ❧

YELLOW FROM THE DUCHY

Mining on Duchy of Cornwall Land in Englishcombe

It has been said that a man dug yellow earth alongside Vernham Wood and sold it to the Fullers' Earth Union in the early days of the industry. This was to the north of Kilkenny Lane and it may be one of the early references to fuller's earth in the parish of Englishcombe found in a number of sources.

Yellow earth was dug by the open cast method and was therefore dependent on good weather. New workings may have been opened as early as 1915, when the Fullers' Earth Union acquired the rights to mine on this land. The deposits were worked with trestles and afterwards the land had to be made good. The records show that new timber was ordered in 1915 for the 'Duchy Development' to build new stables. In addition to open cast mining, by 1916 there was also an adit at Vernham Wood and during the next two years the underground workings became much more extensive, with up to three air shafts. These not only provided ventilation but were also a way of getting the earth up to the Combe Hay works. Yellow earth was essential for many firms engaged in war work at that time.

In 1918, an incline of 1 in 6 was constructed, to connect the 'Duchy' heading directly with the main underground workings linked to the Combe Hay Works. Owen Keevil suggested that two ponies in tandem could pull up the loaded trams, so saving the cost of a winding engine. Later that year, he wanted a pump to drain the heading and the Duchy office agreed to his use of steam for pumping out for eighteen months. The water drained out into the brook in Padleigh Bottom. During that time, the connection between the Duchy and the Combe Hay levels should have been completed. When Bert Upshall started with the company in 1943, he remembers taking his pony 'Nobby' with a train of trams, through the tunnel under the Radstock road (the Fosse Way), to the Duchy.

In September 1919, a Petter-Lister 10bhp oil engine was purchased for underground winding, pulling the trams out of the adit and up an

OS 1932 edition map showing the early Vernham Woods workings. Mining took place on Duchy land between Middle and Vernham Woods during the First World War, when an incline was used to transport the yellow fuller's earth up to Kilkenny Lane. Excavators and dumper trucks were used here later.

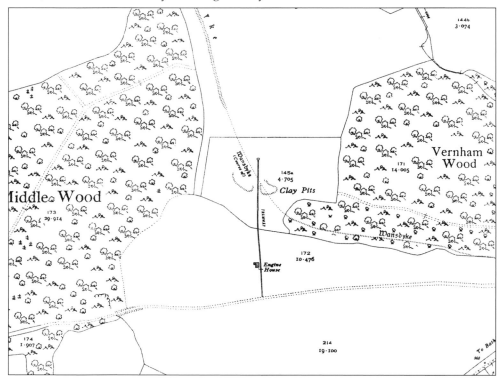

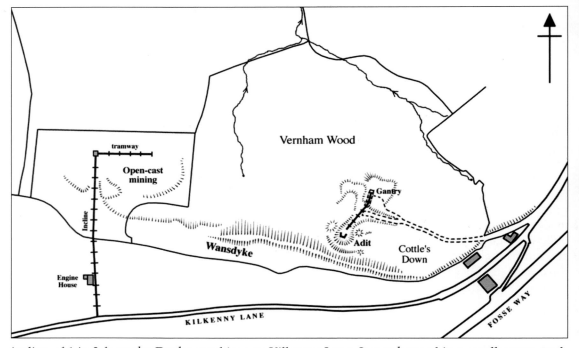

Plan showing the open-cast workings and the new mine in Vernham Wood. The Vernham Wood mine was an expensive failure in the 1960s.

incline of 1 in 3 from the Duchy workings to Kilkenny Lane. It was housed in a small corrugated-iron shed a short distance from the lane. Florrie Parham, who lives nearby on Cottle's Down, on Kilkenny Lane, and whose father Frank Boddy worked in the fuller's earth industry, remembers the Duchy still in operation many years later. She could hear the trams on the incline that worked between the open cast excavations and the lane, where the earth was tipped onto two metal plates and loaded into a lorry for taking round to the works. When the Duchy had first opened, there had been a proposal to run the tramway across both the lane and the main Radstock road into the Combe Hay Works but it is unclear whether this ever happened. There would have been very little road traffic in those days. At these remote sites, there was often a problem with vandalism of the trams, incline or engine house when the plant was not in use. In March 1920, it was commented that the yellow lump from the Duchy always felt very greasy and although it did not look good, it was in fact good fuller's earth. Two months later, a thirty-year lease was obtained on the Duchy of Cornwall workings.

The records of the work in the Duchy area are sparse. They show that there was a fall of earth in the Duchy adit in 1919 and that subsidence in the area occurred in May 1921. A steam crane was in use about that time but its purpose is not mentioned. A new tramway for the open cast mining was installed in February 1921. Thus it appears that, at that time, both underground and open cast mining were in operation.

To win these good deposits of yellow fuller's earth, lying in undulating seams, by open cast mining required the men to first remove a considerable amount of top soil with pick, shovel and barrow. The best yellow was at the bottom of the seam. The men were expected to produce sixteen trams per day. A horse would pull the tram to the bottom of the incline, where it was turned on a steel plate before being wound up to the lane; two side-tipping trams at a time were hauled up. The trams were then pushed back down the hill. By 1932, 5 acres (2ha) of yellow earth were being worked between Middle and Vernham Woods. The work continued until it was no longer economical to get at the earth because of the large amount of topsoil that had to be removed.

Although most yellow earth was obtained from this area, some was found in the underground workings from Combe Hay and a search for further deposits was made in the field to the west of the works, near the offices. In 1942, six new trams, which were to be side-tipping, were required for the yellow earth incline in the Duchy. The incline was some 150 yards (137m) long and a small corrugated-iron shed at the top housed a single-cylinder Petter diesel engine to haul the trams up the slope. The following February, as orders were down, R.W. Nicholds, by now the manager at Redhill, suggested a new incline at the Duchy, the installation of an air motor in a new location and the alignment of a pipeline to the air shaft. The existing incline would have to be concreted because the ground was unstable.

In March 1943, there was a test bore adjacent to Down Wood, further to the southwest, by permission of the Duchy Estate. One seam was 18 inches (0.45m) and another up to 6 feet (1.8m) in depth. Writing to R.H. Robertson in 1958, G.W. Hignett of Southstoke said that blue earth was got from under the Down and West Woods, and a very small amount of yellow from just west of Vernham Wood. There were pits for yellow earth at Middle Wood to the west of Vernham Wood. In 1949, Holmes asked the Duchy Estate for permission to excavate one or two shallow trenches, to establish the location of the Great Fault in this area. At the time, they were driving an underground road towards the public house on Wellsway known as the Burnt House and were anxious to avoid flooding from springs. Trial borings were also carried out to obtain samples of earth.

This area of the Duchy was not affected by the geological fault which was to prevent successful mining towards the north-east. In February 1962, the *Bath Chronicle* recorded the opening of a new mine at Vernham Wood. A new shaft 85 feet (26m) deep was sunk in a rich seam and the men were busy boring a tunnel 450 feet (137m) long out towards the new entry in the wood. This work had actually been started in April 1961 but was held up by solid limestone and flooding due to the springs that were encountered. By this time, they had driven 100 feet (30m) and dynamite had been used. They were now using pneumatic 'clay spaders'. Mr Lloyd Jones, who was in charge of the operation, said that it had been estimated that 100,000 tons of blue fuller's earth lay beneath those fields, although in fact a large part had been excavated previously. Cliffords did all the timberwork for the shaft. A steel gantry at the end of a short tramway was built in Vernham Wood for loading the earth for transport to the works but it was never to be used.

Vernham Wood Mine, newly opened. The manager, Lloyd Jones stands at the entrance to the mine. Unlike most entrances, this one was started from the inside and worked out due to the conditions of the ground. The mine was begun by sinking a shaft to a depth of about 70ft (21.3m).
LAPORTE SOUTHERN NEWS

LEFT: *Vernham Wood Mine entrance with tramway.*
M. YATES/MUSEUM OF BATH AT WORK

BELOW: *The cutting and entrance to the adit in Vernham Wood c1968, some five years after the project was abandoned due to geological problems.*
GORDON & PATRICK HIGGS, GLOUCESTERSHIRE SOCIETY FOR INDUSTRIAL ARCHAEOLOGY

BELOW: *The gantry on the edge of Vernham Wood still standing in 1968. It was to have been used for discharging earth from the mine into a lorry for transporting to the Combe Hay works.*
GORDON & PATRICK HIGGS, GLOUCESTERSHIRE SOCIETY FOR INDUSTRIAL ARCHAEOLOGY

Lloyd Jones had come from the Exeter branch of Laporte's, with three other miners, to sink the shaft along Cottle's Down and drive out from there towards the Duchy. Laporte Industries had taken over the former Fullers' Earth Union in 1954. The scheme was not a success because the workings kept encountering underground springs and the heading continued to fall in. Had it succeeded, it would have enabled the deposits of very good wet earth in the Duchy to be exploited more thoroughly and transported directly into the works via the tramways, rather than by road. There was already a tunnel under the Fosse Way,

Left: *The gantry, looking north.*
M. Yates/Museum of Bath at Work

Below: *The gantry, looking south east.*
M. Yates/Museum of Bath at Work

reinforced with steel arches, though extraction was not permitted within a certain distance of the main road. In the end, the only 'winnings' were those obtained while making the tunnel. It had turned out to be a very expensive failure, due to a geological fault in Woodleaze Field.

In 1963, the Somerset County surveyor enquired about the underground workings alongside Kilkenny Lane, pointing out that the lane was not strong enough to support heavy loads. The Company assured him that no mining would take place within 50 feet (15m) of the road. All earth, from the new development in the Duchy, would be hauled in a 5-ton lorry from the loading bay in Vernham Wood along their own concrete road, which joined the lane beside the house known as 'The Hermitage' on Cottle's Down. It would amount to 100-150 tons per week but, as explained, this was never achieved.

In the final days, all extraction was by the open cast method, being done with a digger. As the seams were undulating it was difficult to get clean skipfuls with the 'Chaseside Loader', a mechanical shovel mounted on a tractor, before being loaded into a dumper truck. The earth was then taken by lorry to the works, on the road constructed through Vernham Wood. This was the least laborious method of extraction. Bert Upshall and Les Pearce were involved in an accident at the Duchy, when the dumper truck overturned with Les on it. Bert managed to push the dumper off by using the 'Chaseside' to free him. The dumper truck could travel at up to 30 mph across the fields!

ABOVE: Photograph of Bert Upshall on the dumper truck. Taken at the open-cast workings in the Duchy down the incline from Kilkennny Lane.
BERT UPSHALL COLLECTION

RIGHT: The vehicles used at the Duchy open-cast site for excavating and transporting the yellow fuller's earth. Bert made sure that Les Pearce did not pick up too much 'muck' with the 'Chaseside', as from the driver's seat it was not easy to see the seam as it undulated.
BERT UPSHALL COLLECTION

NOTES TO CHAPTER 8
A document which may have originated from the National Archives in Kew, is in the South Stoke History Archives, now held in the Bath Record Office. This states that a considerable number of **documents** have been located, which provide legal and general references to the Bath property (of the Fullers' Earth Union?) from early to recent times (*i.e.* to c1951). It states that the area (presumably to be mined) falls within the Duchy, since references commence with the licence/indenture between HRH Prince Edward Albert of Wales (Edward VIII) and Theodore Stretch, plus the Directors, commencing 29th September 1914. Various subsequent leases and assignments follow and correspondence regarding rents and royalties. There is much reference to the Manor of Inglescombe (Ref. 134 to 140). These records may indicate that mining within the Duchy of Cornwall did in fact start around the time of the outbreak of the First World War.

BIBLIOGRAPHY
Article, 'Fuller's Earth Works, Big Bath Extension', *Bath Chronicle*, p11. 17th February 1962
Report, 'New Mine Workings in Vernham Wood', *Laporte Southern News*, c1964
Jean Manco, *The Parish of Englishcombe, A History*, Englishcombe Parish Council, 1995, p22. (Ref. 137 – SRO T/PH/dcl 10, 11: Survey of the Manor of Englishcombe, 1792) '*Around 1800 Charles Hall began to dig fuller's earth from a field above West Wood and sent it to Bristol*'.

Chapter 9

THE BEST YEARS
Expansion 1940-1980

These were the best, the busiest and the most profitable years, according to Bert Upshall, the last foreman at the Combe Hay Works on Odd Down. The war years made for greater difficulties and yet the production of fuller's earth was once again vital to the war effort. Production had to be maintained to meet the demands of foundries and other industries. In October 1939, Combe Hay Works had been producing 120 tons per week and four extra men were needed, three on the kilns and one to feed the mill. By December, there were three miners, a carter, two kilnmen, two mill men and two on the mixing machines. In the same year, the police installed an air raid siren at the works, which could be heard as far away as Newton St Loe. Such was the demand that, by June 1941, five new men were required and the works were now scheduled under the Essential Work Order of 1941.

NEW BUILDINGS AND PLANT

Even in the darkest days of the war, plans were made for further improvements in plant and buildings, and some of these were put into operation almost immediately. R.W. Nicholds, manager at Redhill, proposed an extension of the works at Combe Hay in April 1941, to include a new kiln, dry earth store, mill room and bag store. The aim was to raise production up to 7,000 tons a year. He was also keen to get mains electricity into the works instead of relying on generators. This appears to have been achieved in November 1942 and the Petters automatic lighting set was sold off. When the actual plans for expansion of the works were drawn up, these included roofs, coke yard and gantry, coke furnace and louvre dryer.

Meanwhile on the night of 25-26th April 1942, the works were bombed during the Bath air raid, whilst on the second night, people from Bath sheltered in the fuller's earth mine, which they entered from near the stables in Combe Hay Lane. There was damage to the main building and the mill room roof had to be replaced with asbestos sheeting. The wash house and generator house were both damaged and the fodder house destroyed. Five out of the six water coolers or radiators for the air compressor engines and some of the earlier tanks and containers were holed by enemy machine-gun fire. Despite this, the works were producing again by 4th May.

McIntyre & Sons, Constructional Engineers from Liverpool, had been engaged in March 1942 to draw up plans for the steelwork of the roof over the yard for the wet earth. Highfield and Roger Smith of London designed the roof. The area, to be known as the New Earth Yard for 'green' earth, was covered with asbestos sheeting, to provide a place in which to drop the earth before it was sent up to the crusher located on the top floor in the tower. By this time, the order of operations had been altered so that the earth from the mine was crushed first, before it was dried in the new kiln which was to be a rotary dryer. The new extensions, built by Simplex Concrete Piles Ltd of Redhill, were started in 1943 and completed the following year. The company wanted all these improvements to be ready by 1945. A canopy over the loading bay was installed in July 1948, to prevent the finished earth getting wet as it was being loaded onto lorries for despatch to customers. As the road vehicles got bigger, the canopy had to be extended.

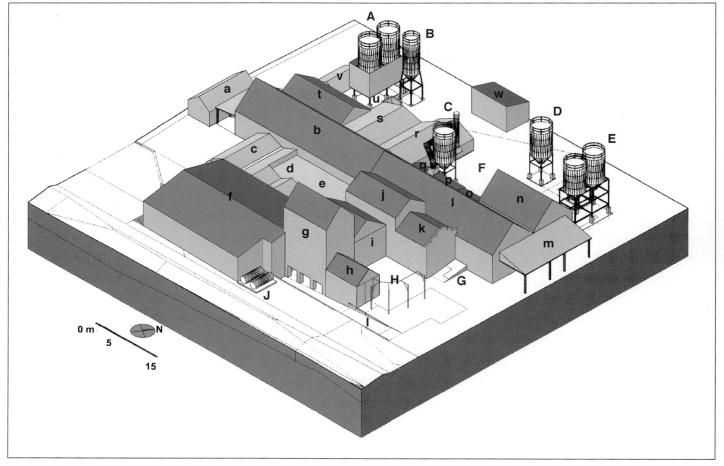

Model view of the Combe Hay works from the east (adapted from a GCP survey). Letters are the same as for the plan, opposite page.

In May 1942, McIntyre & Sons also designed a runway for transporting the coke to the furnace house. This was a bucket, which ran on a gantry into the hopper of the furnace where it was tipped. As this involved considerable handling of the coke, eventually a hole was dug into which the bucket was lowered and filled. The coking hoist was installed in January 1947. The purpose of the coke furnace was to supply a draught of hot air to dry the earth in the rotary dryer. Years later, this furnace was replaced by an oil-fired furnace which required a taller stack. There was a concrete wall round the coke yard and steps down to the old furnace.

New processing machinery was installed in stages. The Cyclone dust extraction plant was commissioned in September 1940. Two Petter diesel engines with cooling tanks, located near the office on the south west side of the buildings, powered the fans in this plant and also the underground ventilation, until all the plant was electrified. A pool provided cooling water for the diesel engines and was used as an emergency water supply during the Second World War.

A Petter diesel engine had been installed the previous November, linked to an automatic lighting system and also driving the blender in the mill room. The steam-driven mill was joined by a second

Plan of the works in the early 1970s before the extensions for the cat litter trade.

KEY: *a.* *Works Office and canopy;* ***b.*** *Oldest part of the present building, which originally had curved corrugated roofs, containing No. 1 mill, dresser, separator, blender, lump and powder elevators and, at the office end, diesel engines for the fans of the dust silo;* ***c.*** *No. 1 steam kiln, which was used after 1943 for stores and later for an office;* ***d.*** *No. 2 steam kiln, which was later used as a mess room and then as a store for soda ash. A fire occurred here in 1966 when being used as a bag store. There were six chutes from each side of the tramway into No's 1 & 2 kilns;* ***e.*** *No's 3 & 4 coke kilns were located here. They were used later to store dry earth. There were four chutes from each side of the tramway into No's 3 and 4 kilns;* ***f.*** *The green earth yard obliterated the tramways to the kilns when extended to the south west in the 1970s, for earth for the cat litter trade. The area contained two crushers and an Aerolift to take the earth up to the louvre dryer in the tower;* ***g.*** *The tower built on Simplex piles during 1944 contained a water tank in the loft, a crusher on the top floor, motors for the dust cyclones on the middle floor, the louvre dryer on the ground floor and an oil fired furnace in the basement;* ***h.*** *The coke furnace building which was fed by a bucket travelling on a gantry from the coke yard until replaced by the oil fired furnace;* ***i.*** *The louvre dryer, owing to its length extended into this area;* ***j.*** *'Worms' under the floor moved the dried earth to the cat litter silos and into the mill room;* ***k.*** *Store for up to 100 tons of dried loose lump earth;* ***l.*** *This building was constructed during 1943. It contained two more mills, a lump elevator and the dust cyclone plant. Sacks of earth were filled, weighed and stored at the eastern end for despatch;* ***m.*** *Canopy over the loading area for lorries;* ***n.*** *Built c.1975 for the cat litter trade. Worms moved the earth to the cat litter silos **E**;*

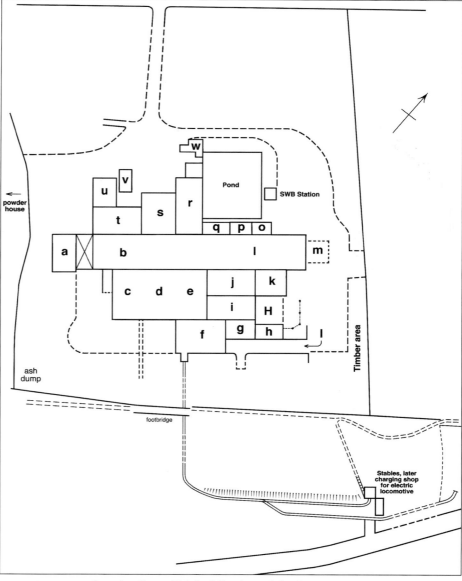

*o. Electrical plant room; **p.** Laboratory; **q.** Electric pumps to move earth to the silos; **r.** This building housed the Garrett steam engine until 1948 and then became a workshop; **s.** A bag store, store room and donkey engine, when the Garrett engine was not in use. **t.** Old warehouse for storing bags; **u.** Weighbridge under the silo **B**; **v.** Weighbridge Room; **w.** Canteen and showers added during the final years; **A.** The two original 50-ton powder silos; **B.** A 25-ton silo which was added later; **C.** The dust extraction plant and silos; **D.** The 75-ton powder silo installed later. For a short time there was a small silo next to it to collect the cat litter dust; **E.** Two cat litter silos; **F.** Site of a pond for cooling water and, during the Second World War, an emergency water supply (EWS). Later it was filled in; **G.** Ramp for the stacker truck; **H.** The old coke yard, later partly roofed over for wet earth; **I.** Ramp down to the green earth yard; **J.** Oil tanks for the oil furnace.*

mill and a blender. A soda hopper, measuring machine, and a 2B 'Dragon' Pulveriser were all installed in the spring of 1943. The 'Lightning' Crusher, proposed in 1942, was installed some time later, along with the Dunford & Elliot Rotary Louvre Dryer in July 1943. It would eventually replace all the old steam and coke kilns.

The plant in the new extension was almost complete by the end of the war in 1945 and most of the machinery had been electrified, including the dust extraction plant. It was planned to do the same to the hoist for the coke furnace. Since the Garrett steam engine was no longer required, it was offered for sale on 22nd November 1949 and the familiar tall smokestack taken down. The Garrett room became a workshop. The old steam-powered winch was replaced by a more powerful electric one in September 1948, which was capable of winding the trams up at 170 feet (52m) a minute. After leaving the forces in 1947, Ed Croker worked first as a miner in the industry but following an accident underground, he was the winchman for a number of years. The system of bells used to give signals was 3 for a start, 1 for stop and 2 for reverse. Ed could look out of the door down to the footbridge, to watch the six trams coming up the incline from the adit near the works. When they arrived, the wooden pegs securing the doors of the trams were knocked out and the earth fell into the chutes. Two years later, the ponies no longer brought the trams to the foot of the incline, having

North-west view of the Combe Hay works in 1988, showing the 75-ton powder silo on the left behind the messroom. The dust extractor silo, right, stands behind some of the oldest buildings.
TONY BROWN

The 25 and 50-ton silos above the weigh-bridge, from the north-west.
TONY BROWN

been replaced by an electric locomotive.

By the end of the Second World War, other uses were found for the old steam kilns. Part of No. 1 was used as an office for a time and as a store room. Soda ash was stored in No. 2 kiln and a place was also made there for the men to have their meal breaks. The coke kilns No's 3 and 4, constructed later than the others and built out from the building, continued to be used up until the late 1950s or early 1960s, for yellow earth from the Duchy. This could not be dried in the louvre dryer but carefully over coke ashes to make YB20. Best blue and yellow were dried on kilns No's 3 and 4. These kilns were also used to produce OK40 powder and also OK lump earth, which was exported to the United States. After that, all earth was dried in the louvre dryer. Gilbert Holley recalled that tramps slept under the kilns in the winter!

In later alterations to the buildings, the basement of the crusher house was made into a store for wet earth, which was little used, whilst the old coke furnace and yard was roofed over in May 1968 and became a separate storage shed, for dry earth from the last adit to be worked. The No. 2 mill room was used for storing the milled powder and it was in this part of the building that the earth was packed in sacks, close to the loading bay at the east end of the building. The capacity of the sacks varied from 55lb (25kg) up to 1.25cwt (64kg).

Above: View from the north. From left to right, the two silos for cat litter granules, the dust extraction plant and the 75-ton powder silo with projecting pipe for discharging the fluidised powder into the awaiting lorries. Beyond are the original two 50-ton silos and the 25-ton powder silo and messroom.
Left: Close-up of the cat litter silos, 70 tons each, on the northern corner of the works. Both Tony Brown

North-east view of the main loading bays, which were extended on the right as the lorries got larger. The sacks were filled in here. The end of the later mill building (mill No. 2) is in the centre and the new extension for the cat litter trade on the right. Tony Brown

Bert's father George Upshall and Stan Love, among other staff, did the packing in this area.

In 1978, a new extension was built to drop the earth used for making granules for the cat litter trade. These were produced upstairs and the bagging took place at the northern corner of the site. A new dust plant was built between the storage silos. There was also a weigh-bridge for the lorries. These had become much heavier in the 1950s, when John Keeling, a local haulier, took over the distribution of the earth. In effect, the Bath works doubled in size during the war years. It was equipped with modern plant, and its products gave excellent results in the foundry industry.

THE MACHINERY OPERATIONS

In 1950, an Aerolift mobile machine with a 10hp Ford petrol engine was used to shovel 12cwt (600kg) of 'green' earth, *i.e.* wet earth from the mine, into a skip which was some 10ft (3m) lower than the floor. The skip was mounted on rails and lifted by a winch to the top of the plant, where it was tipped into the hopper of the jigger-tray, which oscillated back and forward. The skip came down automatically every five minutes to receive another load of earth which was dumped in it by the Aerolift and later by the 'Chaseside'. After a timed period, the earth was sent down a shute to the humming-tray, so-called because of the noise it made and which was later removed, and into the Lightning crusher. This crusher was upstairs on the landing in the tower and inside its inner ring were four square hammers, which smashed the earth against the baffle plate on the back wall of the mill. This crusher was not satisfactory for wet earth, which became clogged between the hammers and baffle plate. A more modern Lightning crusher, supplied by the Patent Lightning Crusher Co., was installed in 1970. It was capable, for example, of crushing up to 15 tons of fuller's earth in an hour.

From there, it went straight down a shute, later replaced by an endless belt, into the rotary dryer.

East view taken during the post-war period. Compare with the same view taken in 1988, below.
BATH EVENING CHRONICLE

East view of the old corrugated-iron furnace building, extreme left, the dry earth store, centre, and the mill building (mill No. 2), right. Behind the loading bays is the later storage building for cat litter, with its silos.
TONY BROWN

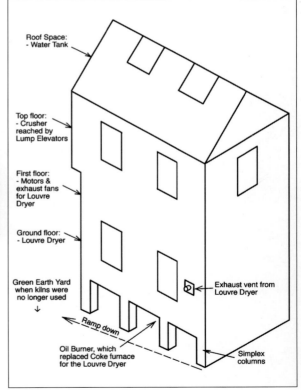

FAR RIGHT: Diagram of the Tower

Hot air from the coke furnace, later oil-fired, was drawn into the dryer by a fan. At the opposite end, another fan, located on the floor above the dryer, drew out the moisture in the form of steam, which was then discharged to the outside air. The louvre dryer revolved on four rollers. Around 30cwt (1,500kg) of wet earth were fed in at one end of this long cylindrical oven every five minutes, so that within an hour, over fifteen tons of dried earth could be produced. Such was the efficiency of the louvre dryer that the earth was in it for only about one hour, the time being regulated according to the moisture level required. When the louvre dryer was installed, it meant that the dried and milled earth products could be sold to the foundries.

The dried earth was then ready to be milled and graded. Originally, this was done in the dresser, a revolving drum which sieved the fuller's earth through gauzes or silks according to the degree of fineness required in the powder. It had three doors on each side and was fed with the dried and crushed earth from the powder elevator. The coarser material, known as SP4 or AT, passed through the gauzes (100 mesh), while the finer powder came through the silks (200 mesh) and down through the worm, and was then taken off into sacks and sewn up. The material that did not get through was returned via the lump elevator to the mill and via the powder elevator shute to the dresser to be recycled. The powder coming out of the dresser used to feel like hot water and could be said to almost flow into the sacks on the scales! After being sewn up they were taken on the sack trucks to be stacked ready for delivery.

Eventually, this dresser was replaced by two Stag air separators. The separator was fed by the powder elevator, which had larger and wider buckets than the lump elevator. On the top, there were four handles operating a screw thread, which could be adjusted to vary the coarseness or fineness of the powder required. Below this, a fan blew the finest powder to the outside of the separator through a big revolving cone and this collected at the bottom of the separator, which could hold between a half to one ton of powdered earth. A valve was then opened to fill the sacks waiting on the scales. The tailings were the coarser particles and these passed out of the separator, down

ABOVE: View from the south of the office building, left, in which many of the documents on which this research is based were found in 1988. To the right of the covered way were the cooling tanks for the Petter diesel engines, in front of No. 1 millroom, the oldest of the original mill buildings. No. 1 kiln was on the extreme right.
TONY BROWN

LEFT: The south-west end wall of No. 1 millroom, with the doorway through to the office outside.
TONY BROWN

down to 2 inch (50mm) lumps to reduce the earth to a workable size. It was then dried to lower the moisture content from between 20-40% to 5-10% and finally the earth was separated by size, to make both powder and granular products.

PRODUCTS AND CUSTOMERS

In January 1941, Nicholds found that a blend of fuller's earth with soda ash made a suitable substitute for Bentonite (a clay with similar properties to calcium montmorillonite) but if the soda ash arrived in a wet condition it was useless. Imperial Chemical Industries (ICI) were the suppliers of light or anhydrous sodium carbonate, known as soda ash. By April, there was a dramatic increase in the demand for a new blend of powder with soda ash. This was named 'Union Bentonite' and had a moisture content of 9.8%, involving experimentation with different combinations of coke and cinders in the kilns to get this level of moisture. The Ministry of Works forecast a demand for Union Bentonite of 10,000 tons per year. Combe Hay would therefore have had to produce 250 tons per week when at that time it was only 100 tons. This product was later renamed Fulbond No. 1 and No. 2. Fulbond No. 1 was completely free of moisture and contained no soda ash whereas No's 2 and 3 had soda ash added. Fulbent had more moisture than Fulbond.

Union Bentonite was very important to the war effort as it was used in a number of crucial industries, such as foundries and in

the tailing shute, through the worm and into the lump elevator, there to go through the mill and the whole process again. The No. 2 mill, which had been installed in May 1943, had produced 12,000 tons of powder by July 1946.

In the final years of the industry, the earth which arrived at the works from the last adit by lorry was graded and crushed into 4 inch (100mm) lumps and then through a second crusher

Interior of No. 1 millroom in 1988. The arch into No. 2 millroom is visible at the end, together with the arched entrances to two of the kilns on the right. The boiler room was on the left. TONY BROWN

paint manufacturing. Such was the demand for all these products that, by 1942, the works could not supply all that was being asked for and were told to concentrate on YB20, Fulbond 3 and UB No. 1. Boots the Chemists took 'blue lump' and the men were reminded that this had to be turned after the first night's firing, with the second night's firing, using the residual heat in the cinders, to complete the drying.

In March 1942, Nicholds again reminded Combe Hay that great care was needed in drying SP4 – it was not to be just 'cover-dried'. He appreciated that there were problems if the wind was from the north-east, as this caused the fire to burn out more quickly. By the end of the Second World War, it was necessary to get production up to 250 tons a week and two shifts were considered to meet this demand. Other

View from the north-west of the old boilerhouse for the Garratt steam plant, later used for a workshop. Note the openings in the end wall for the belt drive through to the lay shaft in No. 1 millroom.
TONY BROWN

problems in the post-war years were a severe shortage of soda ash from ICI at Northwich, shortage of coke and power cuts every twelve days. Despite this, there was probably a record output for one day in September 1948, when 160 tons were despatched. The plant started getting much busier after the war, with a growing demand from the expanding oil industry.

When the louvre dryer was shut down in August 1945, the manager, Tom Holmes, was told to concentrate on UB, and Fulbond 2 and 3, and that only SP4 was to be dried on the kilns. The next year, it was decided to use the Garrett engine to prepare AT20, as the electric mill could not produce the required fineness of powder. The Anglo-American Oil Co. used Fulbent 150 but were now asking for 140, this being a finer powder. When the Shell Oil Company complained, in October 1948, that at their oilfields Fulbent 182 was 'frothing' in the drill bore, Holmes found it was best produced when the weather was warm and dry. He had reduced the quantity of soda ash and increased the moisture content. A tester was employed from around the 1950s to check samples of the products before they were dispatched. Trade in fuller's earth became very brisk in May 1951, with the introduction of the rearmament programme.

Following a visit to Morocco in November 1946, Nicholds arranged for a substantial quantity of earth from there to be sent to Combe Hay. Holmes suggested that this should be stored in the old No. 4 kiln but in fact it was stored under the dryer house and possibly at Midford, which was no longer being used to produce earth. Further consignments of North African earth came from Algeria, via the Bristol docks, during the following years and 1,000 tons had to be stored in the firing chambers of the old kilns and on one of the kiln floors. It was heavy work, as the earth was loose, not in sacks, and required a great deal of moving with spade and barrow. It was also very moist and easily blocked the louvre dryer. Some of this earth was ordered to make Fulbond T, which was milled for steelworks in

the United Kingdom.

It was about the time that Laporte Industries Limited took over the Fullers' Earth Union in 1954 that Jim Woolman joined the work force. His first job was shifting 250 tons of white clay, which had come to Bristol docks from Algeria, and by lorry to Combe Hay Works. This was put in the kilns, milled and mixed with both kinds of local fuller's earth. In the mill room there were two shifts at that time, from 6am until 2pm and from 2pm until 10pm, with two men on each shift. Their target was to produce eighteen tons, which was then bagged in either 1cwt (50kg) paper or 2cwt (100kg) hessian sacks. He found that his hands became dried out working with milled fuller's earth and would use a grease to stop them splitting.

The early 1960s were another time of expansion in the industry, with an increasing demand for earth, most of which was used in foundries for bonding and in the oil refining industry. In August 1966, there was a fire in the bag store which destroyed 5,000 bundles of sacks, each containing some fifty paper sacks! Fortunately, a stack of full bags of fuller's earth prevented the fire from spreading to the rest of the factory but serious damage was done to the roof.

By the end of the industry in Bath, the earth was either marketed in granular form or ground to a fine powder. The addition of small amounts of soda ash (2-6%), prior to the drying and grinding, converted the fuller's earth when wetted again into sodium montmorillonite or Bentonite. By varying the amount of soda ash, different grades of Bentonite were produced.

A FINAL PORTRAIT OF THE WORKS

Just a year before the plant closed, the manager recorded that nineteen men were employed on three shifts and that this included one electrician, one fitter and one foreman fitter, who was in charge of the stores. There were a further six staff, namely the manager, deputy manager, office manager, works foreman, mine foreman and a works tester or chemist.

Stan Love and George Upshall stacking the fuller's earth (Fulbond) near the loading bay. This was cold and windy work, especially in the winter.
BERT UPSHALL COLLECTION

One of the last managers at Combe Hay, Horace Beech, described the production situation as it existed in the late 1970s:

'In the last few years of operation, the processing plant consisted of two crushers, one oil fired louvre dryer, two Johnson grinding roller mills, two Stag air separators and two fine mesh dressing machines. By this stage the product was mainly fluidised by low-pressure compressors, working at 15lbs per sq.in (1kg/sq.cm) and delivering 208cu.ft (6cu.m) per minute, to transport it to the storage silos. Two hundred tons per week was then despatched in 50kg bags and three hundred tons left the works in bulk tankers.'

The Avon County Council report, *Mineral Working in Avon*, 1978, contained a similar description:

'Processing takes the form of crushing, drying and milling, and the final product may then be bagged or stored in bulk silos. The raw clay passes through two crushers, a primary jaw crusher and a secondary toothed roll crusher, and is then dried in a rotary oven. It then passes to the mill, where it is ground to a particle size less than 75 microns (200 mesh). Processing is thus fairly simple, there being none of the chemical treatments that are carried out at other plants in the country. The fuller's earth from the Bath area is not suitable for acid treatment as it contains up to 30% of calcite. The only specialised process in Avon is the separation before milling of 7mm granules. These are stored and bagged and have a ready market as cat litter ... Some dust is produced by the plant, especially during the dry weather, but this is not a serious problem, since there is no chemical processing there are no waste products to be disposed of ... For reasons of confidentiality production figures for the mine cannot be disclosed. However, the small output has risen steadily over the last 20 years and reached a peak in 1971. Since that date production has declined slightly and this trend is similar to that shown by the national fuller's earth industry.'

RIGHT: *The Dunford & Elliott Rotary Louvre Dryer, which eventually replaced all the kilns. The revolving kiln was approximately 24ft in length, with a diameter of 8ft. Hot air drawn through the dryer by fans removed the moisture and so enabled the water content of the earth to be controlled more accurately.*
FROM A SKETCH BY GILBERT HOLLEY

BELOW: *Drawing of a Stag Separator. The Stag Separator rotated at high speed. The heavier particles of dried and milled fuller's earth were then recycled, whilst the finer powder was discharged, weighed and bagged.*
FROM A SKETCH BY BERT UPSHALL

BELOW: *Perspective drawing of the Rotary Dryer.*
FROM A SKETCH BY BERT UPSHALL

ROTARY LOUVRE DRYER

Two views of the primary earth breaker (or 'kibbler') in the green earth yard, taken in July 1984 when the machinery at the works was being dismantled.
DAVID POLLARD

Taken at the same time, showing the primary earth breaker on the left, and the second crusher and conveyor belt, which took the earth from the green yard up to the louvre dryer on the floor above, with a walkway for the men, on the right.
DAVID POLLARD

Two years after this report, mining ceased and the works at Combe Hay closed at the beginning of 1980. This had been announced in the previous July, following the loss of an important customer, Dartmouth Auto Castings Ltd in the West Midlands, which was closing. The Company works manager, John Crampton, stated that this meant the loss of fifty jobs and it marked the end of almost one hundred years of mining fuller's earth in the area.

NOTES TO CHAPTER 9

For details about the different products see **Appendix 2**.

Bentonite is a naturally occurring clay which has similar but enhanced properties to fuller's earth (calcium montmorillonite). It is named after Fort Benton, Wyoming in the USA.

The Dunford & Elliott **Louvre Rotary Dryer** (later Newell Dunford Engineering Ltd) was designed to produce evenly dried earth. The problem with drying in the kilns had been that the outside of a lump of earth became overdried, while the inside remained moist. In the louvre dryer, it was possible to dry evenly sized and graded pellets in an atmosphere almost saturated with water for some uses. The operator could regulate the time spent in the dryer according to the level of moisture required. The interior louvres acted like a screw, moving the earth along inside the cylinder from the entry to where it was discharged.

A double-roll **'kibbler'** was used for breaking up hard clays into small lumps suitable for further grinding, although David Pollard calls the machinery at the Combe Hay Works, 'primary earth breakers'. The term 'kibbler' was used elsewhere to describe a machine to break up the lumps of clay, from the verb '*to kibble*', *i.e.* to grind fairly coarsely.

BIBLIOGRAPHY

The Avon County Council report, *Mineral Working in Avon*, 1978
Article on the contribution of the industry to the war effort, *Bath Chronicle*, July 1945
Article on the fire in the Bag Store at the Fuller's Earth Works, *Bath Chronicle*, 13th August 1966
Article on Prince Charles' visit to the works with Derek Oliver (deputy manager), *Bath Chronicle*, 26th July 1972
Press announcement of the impending closure of the Fuller's Earth Works at Combe Hay, *Bath Chronicle*, 26th July 1979
Donald Mullins, 'Fuller's Earth in Somerset', *The Somerset Countryman*, Vol. 17, No. 11, July-Sept. 1953, p291f.

Fuller's Earth production in the United Kingdom, 1948-1974, showing the steady rise in production. The large and increasing output from the Bath area contributed to this rise, especially after WW2.
MINERAL RESOURCES CONSULTATIVE COMMITTEE MINERAL DOSSIER NO. 3 – FULLER'S EARTH

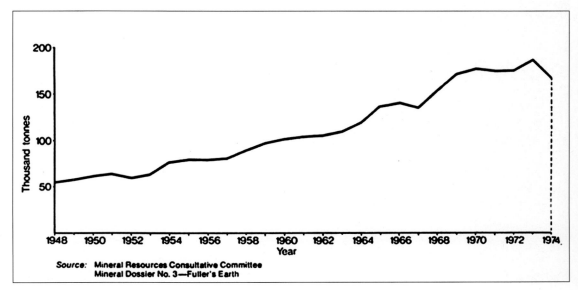

Source: Mineral Resources Consultative Committee Mineral Dossier No. 3—Fuller's Earth

⊰ Chapter 10 ⊱
TRANSPORT TALES
Road, Railway and Canal

The Romans wisely sited their *fullonicae* near deposits of fuller's earth wherever possible and even then, rarely more than a day's waggon journey away from one. The reason was, as Robertson has pointed out, that to transport fuller's earth over long distances was difficult and costly. It was either packed in casks or sent loose in a waggon.

The Somersetshire Coal Canal was an obvious asset to the early developers of the Tucking Mill site and also that at Hodshill. No documentary evidence has been found as to the amount of 'finished' earth transported on the canal nor when the last despatch was made. The wharf opposite the mill at Tucking Mill would also have been used to bring in coal for the furnace. Later, after the canal was

The Somersetshire Coal Canal at Tucking Mill. A cart, belonging to William Hamlen, said to be loaded with blue rock stone from the Emborough Quarries, is passing the entrance to the fuller's earth works. The carter was one of Hamlen's sons and the man in the top hat was known as 'Copper Sir'. The horses were named 'Prince', 'Captain', 'Trooper' and' Mother's Gray'.
Dr E. Smith collection

An overall view of the GWR goods yard and goods shed at Bath station in 1910. The men holding poles and posing for the photographer are shunters.

abandoned, it was brought down from Midford railway goods yard. The tonnage rate being charged on the Grand Junction Canal around 1831 for fuller's earth is listed as $^1/_2$d and for coal $^3/_4$d per ton per mile and it is possible that similar rates applied on the Somersetshire Coal Canal.

The proximity of the Somerset & Dorset Joint Railway to Tucking Mill also provided a useful means of despatching fuller's earth from the works there. During 1893, the agent engaged by the railway company to haul the fuller's earth complained of the steep grades up from Tucking Mill, to the goods siding to the south of Midford station. He stated that unless the haulage rate was substantially improved, he would withdraw his services. As a consequence of this, in the following year, the Joint Committee of the railway company submitted plans for a new siding adjacent to the Tucking Mill Lane. This small goods yard, to the north of the station, opened at the end of 1894. The yard was also used by William Hamlen & Sons for their coal merchants' business, established by 1897. Hamlens were engaged to haul fuller's earth from Tucking Mill for a number of years, using horses and carts at first and later their brown liveried lorries. In some weeks, as much as two

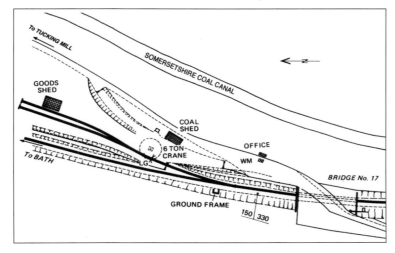

Plan of Midford goods yard. This yard, sited to the north of the station, was where the fuller's earth from Tucking Mill was loaded and despatched to many different destinations.

hundred tons were despatched and they would also have delivered coal to the works. For a time, coal, from pits higher up the Cam Valley, was unloaded at the Tucking Mill canal wharf for both the fuller's earth works and the pumping station of the Combe Down Water Works, to the west of the railway viaduct.

In 1923, Owen Keevil wrote to the Somerset & Dorset Joint Railway at Bath Midland station (it was renamed Bath Green Park by BR in 1951) as to what notice was required if the company decided to give up possession of the stacking ground at Midford siding and also the store there. As a result these two facilities were given up the next year. There were often complaints from customers that the fuller's earth had reached them in a damp state. Keevil therefore wanted all open railway wagons to be double sheeted or, preferably, that covered goods vans be used.

The siding at Midford was still being used as late as 1953 for despatching earth. At times, a whole day would be spent loading three to four goods vans, filling them to the top with acid-activated earth, which had been produced at Redhill and stored temporarily at Tucking Mill. It was destined for the oil refinery at Llandarcy in South Wales. The goods yard finally closed in June 1963.

There was considerable correspondence with the railway companies, in which they were challenged to offer more favourable rates. There were numerous complaints about delays, misdirection and damage to the fuller's earth in transit to the customers. This usually meant that the product had got wet and was therefore useless. In the early days, each consignee had their own supply of sacks or they

Midford Goods Yard. The goods shed is in the right middle background of the view. It was essential to keep the fuller's earth dry when being transported. Former LM&S Class '4F' No. 44422, built at Derby in 1927, passes Midford goods yard with the 12.35pm freight from Bath to Evercreech Junction on 4th March 1955. Note the box vans in the yard which were used to transport fuller's earth, together with Ivo Peters' faithful old Bentley MYD 50.
THE IVO PETERS COLLECTION

*Yorkshire steam waggon U3683. One of the Yorkshire steam waggons used by the Fullers' Earth Union at Bath, which appears to have brought a load of fuller's earth in sacks to the goods yard and may be later returning to the works with pit props, seen in the railway wagon behind. The lettering on the side of the waggon appears to read 'FULLERS' EARTH UNION LTD. MIDFORD WORKS N*R.* BATH'. The photograph was probably taken at the GWR goods yard in Bath. James Staddon stands on the left and Albert 'Smacker' Gerrish is on the right, leaning against the waggon. The man on the far right is probably Herbert Patch, a stoker at Tucking Mill.*

were charged by the Fullers' Earth Union for new sacks. The non-return or late return of these sacks was a continuing problem and resulted in much correspondence with the customers concerned.

H.N. Garrett had his own horses, 'Bob' and 'Major', which were stabled behind Tucking Mill Cottage and in the care of a carter named Bill Seal. When Garrett's company was wound up and acquired by the Fullers' Earth Union in 1915, Hamlens took over the haulage requirements. These included taking best blue earth from Combe Hay to the Top Works and transporting pit props from the Midford railway goods yard to the Combe Hay Works. Hamlens' horses at about that time were 'Prince', 'Captain', 'Trooper' and 'Mother's Gray' according to Walter Hamlen, one of William's sons. Later, a road was put in which enabled Hamlens' lorry, purchased around 1930, to get in closer to the works at Tucking Mill for loading. The improved access replaced the winch and cable that were in use when Hamlens' used a horse and cart.

Sometimes Stan Wicks would be sent up to Hamlens' yard, near the centre of Midford, with a note to ask them to come down and fetch a load of fuller's earth, perhaps one or two tons. They would come with a wagon and three to four horses. Stan and his sister Gwen, who, as children, lived in Tucking Mill House in the early 1920s, and Vera Morris from the cottage, would sometimes walk behind Hamlens' cart up to Midford and get a ride back to Tucking Mill. The horses broke into a gallop to overcome the gradient into the siding. After the use of horse and carts, steam waggons, made by the Yorkshire Commercial Motor Company, were used. Owen Keevil hoped to purchase one of these before the end of 1915 but it was eventually collected in March 1916. Two of these were in use for over ten years. There are a number of interesting stories told about them and their drivers, one of whom was a colourful character known as 'Smacker' Gerrish from his ability in the boxing ring. Among his duties, he was sent with a steam lorry to get coal from the local mines, when it was not being delivered by Hamlens, as well as transporting the earth between sites and to the railway goods yards.

There was a water standpipe near the road at Top Works, just before the descent past Midford Castle. This belonged to the Fullers' Earth Union and when Owen Keevil discovered that drivers of other steam waggons were refilling their boilers from it, he had it secured with a lock and key! The next year, Keevil was in dispute with the Midland Railway over getting water for the steam waggons at Bath Midland Road goods yard. It was essential that they refilled prior to the climb back up to Combe Hay. The railway company wanted to charge the Fullers' Earth Union but Keevil pointed out that the company was providing the railway with several thousand tons of traffic every year. He was also in dispute with the railway for losing bags, in which the earth was transported, and over the unloading of pit props from railway wagons, when his men required some help from railway staff.

The Coal Controller wished to requisition both steam waggons in 1918, under wartime requirements. It appears that in fact only wagon No. 1 was requisitioned by the Bath Electric Tramways and then only for a fairly short time. Keevil discussed with that company the use of 'Phoenix Briquettes', presumably as an alternative fuel for the steam waggons.

The steam waggons had solid rubber tyres and in 1918, Keevil believed that these were being damaged by cuts caused by old steam plates from the kilns, which had been laid at the Top Works to form a base for shovelling the earth, either from the nearby workings or that brought from Combe Hay. In 1923, he negotiated with the Bath Tramways Motor Company for the fitting of new tyres to the steam waggons, mentioning in passing that he had had experience of these vehicles since 1910. In the mid-1920s, six were stationed at Redhill and two at Combe Hay but latterly there was only one in Bath.

Quite an adventure surrounded the collecting of steam waggon No. 4 from Redhill in July 1918. On the journey to Bath, a fire was started in a field beside the road between Redhill and Newbury, despite the waggon being fitted with a spark arrester. The vehicle still threw out a tremendous quantity of live coals when going uphill with a load, whilst the draught was tremendous. Apparently, when firing, a piece of coal weighing almost 15lbs (7kg) would be pulled out of the fireman's hand into the firebox as easily as if it were a feather and it required considerable force when running to pull open the fire door!

The crew on the waggon were held up at every town right through to Melksham, timed between each town and a detective rode with them on the waggon from Foxhill into Hungerford! The men noticed that he looked at his watch when he mounted the waggon and when he got off, and they thought he intended to catch them speeding. The driver, Frank Bennett, got wise to what was happening and drove along at a steady 5mph all the way and when questioned about the speed of the waggon, he said it was a new one and he was driving her steadily all the way to Bath! Bennett, Gerrish and Keevil were sent a summons by the Bath police to appear at Reading magistrates' court for '*without lawful authority or excuse causing damage by setting fire to growing grass and cut hay on July 1st.*' The outcome is unknown.

Later, this same vehicle was involved in an accident at the Midland Railway goods yard with a horse waggon, when the brass front rail of the steam waggon was flattened. It was sent away for repair and No. 5 waggon, often driven by Jim Staddon, was sent from Redhill. Steam waggons required a lot of maintenance. Springs broke, and the brake linings only lasted a few months, perhaps due to the steep hills around Bath. They were not very economical and Keevil would have preferred a Sentinel steam waggon, like the one at Redhill, which was proving to be speedier, more economical on water and fuel, and easier to handle and maintain but was more expensive to purchase.

From 1st January 1921, the road tax on the waggon was £30 and the licence had to be displayed

Above: One of the road hauliers in Bath for fuller's earth, the City Steam Transport Company, was based in this depot on the Lower Bristol Road. The depot was later taken over by Guest Transport Services and is now used by Unigate Dairies for their milk floats.
MIKE CHAPMAN

on the left-hand side of the vehicle. The following March, it was decided to exchange the Bath steam waggons with Redhill and Willis stayed in Surrey one weekend to overhaul his vehicle prior to driving it back to Bath. Steam was to be raised at 3am, with departure at 4am. On the way back to Bath, the driver got lost and W.F. Keevil said to his son Owen that Willis was still *'roaming about in the wilderness seeking the promised land'* and he hoped that *'the vehicle will not rust out before it reaches Bath!'* Willis arrived in Bath about 3pm the next day, when normally the journey took around twelve hours.

Stan Wicks remembered how, in 1924, when his father William was sacked from Tucking Mill works over a confrontation with the stoker, his family exchanged houses with Ernie West, the new foreman. The steam waggon was used to transport the furniture between the houses and coming down Frome Road, sparks from the chimney set fire to Mr West's bedding. Such was the noise from the lorry that the driver, 'Smacker' Gerrish, could not hear the cries to stop. When they arrived at Mr Hamlen's house in the centre of Midford, everyone jumped on the mattress to extinguish the fire! Edward Densley recalled that, at the age of twelve, he used to walk from his home at Odd Down to the works, where his father was the charge-hand miller of the day. 'Smacker' would give him a shilling to clean and polish the Yorkshire, while he went to the Burnt House Inn to quench his thirst.

Around 1925, the Company attempted to sell the waggons for £60 each. Two years later, Keevil was in contact with two haulage contractors to say that he had two Yorkshire steam waggons for a quick sale at £55 each. The waggons were finally sold in 1929. For a short time, the Combe Hay Works used a Sentinel DG6 steam lorry. Shellard, the driver of this vehicle, was caught by the police at Swindon in May 1929 for overloading the waggon, which was licensed to carry between 12 and 15 tons.

In the 1930s, the Company decided to employ outside contractors to transport the fuller's earth and bring in coal, coke and wood. Owen Keevil, by now in charge at Redhill, wrote to Nicholds, the manager at Combe Hay, saying that trade did not warrant the Fullers' Earth Union having their own vehicles. One of the road hauliers was a Bath company, the City Steam Transport Company, based in the Lower Bristol Road. By 1933, that company had a new 6-wheeled Sentinel, a diesel-engined Foden and a 6-wheeled petrol-engined Garner lorry, and was contracted to carry out the transport requirements for the next year. For example, in July 1933, they transported miners' powder in sacks from Combe Hay Works to the Great Western Railway goods yard in Bath, for transit to the coalfields. In the same month, another local haulier, the Bath Roadway Services on the Upper Bristol Road, was hired for deliveries to London.

Over the years, a considerable quantity of earth was despatched by sea. Charles Hill & Sons were the shipping agents used by the Fullers' Earth Union at Bristol, where the fuller's earth was sent out from the docks in ships of the Bristol City Line, including in October 1913 the SS *New York*. Records of the Canadian Pacific Railway Company's steamship services show that, during the First World War

and thereafter, there were regular despatches of fuller's earth in barrels or 2cwt bags to Canada and the USA from Avonmouth, the agents in the USA being L.A. Salomon & Bro., Pearl Street, in New York City. The GWR, the MR and the S&DJR were used to transfer the earth from Bath to the docks, where it was carried by such ships as the SS *Montcalm*, SS *Montfort* and SS *Batsford*. The manager, R.W. Nicholds, was to write to Coast Lines in 1936 '*It is of the utmost importance the material is kept bone dry, also that no sack hooks must be used on the bags*'. The bags were in fact marked 'No Hooks. Keep Dry'. The docks at Bristol were frequently used for the import of certain kinds of earth from Germany up until the Second World War and from North Africa after the war. The finished products were then exported from Bristol and other ports to the United States, the Dominions and other destinations overseas. Coastal shipping companies, such as Coast Lines, were used for exports to Ireland and Scotland. Some consignments were sent by road to the docks in London.

In the closing years of the industry, road transport was used to bring the raw earth from the mines to the works for processing, along the public highways. This included both the Duchy opencast site and also the last adit off Combe Hay Lane, from which the earth was extracted. A lorry was loaded from the concrete loading bay there by a shovel mounted on a Massey Ferguson tractor and transported round to the main works.

According to Jim Summers, after World War Two a number of different hauliers were engaged.

An aerial view of Avonmouth Docks circa 1935. Much of the fuller's earth from the Bath area was exported through these docks to be shipped overseas and also to markets nearer home, in Ireland and Scotland. Fison's also later established a factory here at Avonmouth using fuller's earth to make fertiliser.
NEIL PARKHOUSE COLLECTION

John Keeling's AEC flat bed articulated lorry registration number EGL 772F at his depot in Red Lion Quarry. For many years, his company transported the fuller's earth to a number of destinations in the UK.
MARION & ALAN KEELING

John Keeling & Son's articulated tanker D27 HOU, a Volvo FH12. John was later joined by his son Alan. When much of the fuller's earth was fluidised, tanker lorries were used to transport the product to customers.
MARION & ALAN KEELING

Guest Transport Services were succeeded by British Road Services. When that organisation got into difficulties, John Keeling & Son, who had taken over Hamlen's business in 1953, transported fuller's earth until production ended at Combe Hay Works. At first, the fuller's earth was despatched in sacks but it was later sent in bulk tankers. Keelings also brought in soda ash from the chemical industry, which was required for mixing with the earth to make a product similar to bentonite.

NOTES TO CHAPTER 10

H. Garner of Moseley, Birmingham, built lorries from 1915 from parts imported from the USA. In 1925, he produced his own design, a two-ton lorry with a Dorman engine. The firm moved to Tyldesley in 1926 and, in 1931, brought out a new range of lorries of up to six tons payload. From 1934-6, the company was Sentinel-Garner at Shrewsbury and it was resold in 1936 to an ex-Dodge Consortium. (Paul Lewis, *Encyclopaedia of Trucks*)

BIBLIOGRAPHY

Arlett, M.J., *The Railways of Midford*, Somerset & Dorset Railway Trust, 1983

Arlett, M.J., *The Somerset & Dorset at Midford*, Millstream Books, 1986

Judge, C.W., & Potts, C.R., *An Historical Survey of the Somerset & Dorset Railway*, Oxford Publishing Co., 1979

Parfitt, R., *The History of Southstoke and Midford*, 2001

Chapter 11

CLAYS TO CREAMS
Products for a Worldwide Market

A HUNDRED AND ONE USES!

In 1890, on the eve of the creation of the Fullers' Earth Union Ltd, Cawley & Co. described their fuller's earth as: '*Blue, yellow, drab, kiln dried, raw, prepared for cloth, flannel and silk manufacturing; ground and prepared for refining oils, petroleum wax etc; prepared and specially levigated for toilet and other purposes*'. Over the following years, this variety of uses was to be considerably extended as more and more applications were discovered for this amazing clay. Such was the success of the Fullers' Earth Union in those early days that the company obtained the highest award at the Chicago Exhibition of 1893. Four years later, it won the Gold Medal at Brussels and again achieved the highest award in Paris in 1900. By 1954, when acquired by Laporte Industries, the company had developed into one of the largest producers in the world of activated earths, and other montmorillonite and bentonite products.

The Avon County Council report, *Mineral Working in Avon*, 1978, summarised the applications of fuller's earth as follows:

'*The properties of absorption (attraction and adherence of material to the body of the mineral) and adsorption (adherence of material to the surface of the mineral) give rise to the classic 'fulling' uses of the clay as a cleansing agent and absorbent. Its bonding ability is used to bond foundry moulding sand, and this is one of its most important uses. This property is also applicable to pelletising iron ore concentrates and animal feedstuffs. The main outlets for the earth from Combe Hay are to the motor industry for foundry moulding sands, to the agricultural industries for fertilisers and cattle feed additives and the specialised markets of pet litter and cosmetics.*'

The nature of the customers and the destinations indicate how varied and widespread were the uses of fuller's earth from Bath.

1. FULLING AND DYEING

The actual process of fulling, the thickening and shrinking of the cloth by felting the fibres, was carried out by using fulling stocks or heavy wooden hammers with which to pound the cloth. This was the one textile machine that had been successfully mechanised. It was sometimes also called 'milling'. This was a preliminary to the second fulling, which used a weaker mixture of fuller's earth and, with a typical broadcloth, took many hours.

The finishing sequence of the cloth began with scouring it with fuller's earth to remove oil and size. The oil had been inserted before carding and the size applied before weaving. Scouring also removed any dirt that had been collected on the way. Later in the sequence, there was '*milling or fulling with soap and warm water, either in the fulling stocks or in an improved milling machine*'. Fuller's earth was also used for cleaning the wool after weaving. Fullers did not require the earth they used to be ground to a powder because dried fuller's earth, even in lump form, dispersed easily when put into water.

The medieval concentration of the prosperous woollen industry in the West of England has been attributed to the abundant supplies of both fuller's earth and, to raise the nap on the finished cloth, teazels! Here, the most heavily fulled cloths were made, beginning with broadcloth, often black, which was used for important men's suiting for centuries. The fine short wool required for broadcloths came from sheep on the Mendips or on the Wiltshire and Dorset downlands. In the same area, it was dyed with 'Bristol Red' and it was this cloth that was later used in the British Army, hence the term 'red coats'. The need for fuller's earth grew as sheep were bred with coarser and longer wool, and so had a higher proportion of wool grease which had to be removed. Blue and yellow fuller's earth was preferred by cloth manufacturers for different cloths in Yorkshire. Blue was used for broadcloth, while yellow was preferred for kerseymeres and superfine cloth.

In the 19th century, the two main uses of fuller's earth were for 'earthing' the cloth after dyeing and in the rinse after milling. This earthing was done to obtain fastness to rubbing. The earth was serving here as a mordant, the dye reacting with the fuller's earth to form an insoluble substance which attaches to the fibres of the cloth. One ton of fuller's earth could produce up to ten tons of sludge, deposited in the settling tanks in the woollen industry. In the 20th century, fuller's earth has been used to remove the surplus dark blue colours from the serge cloth used for school uniforms, up to the time of the Second World War. In both world wars, it was used as a substitute for soap in the treatment of coarse blankets, and in the earthing of dark naval and other uniforms. Today, various other substances have been used, such as soap mixtures with an ammoniacal base, to replace fuller's earth in these processes.

It was claimed that Tucking Mill made the best fuller's earth for fulling, because the grit had been removed by Dames' slurrying and settling process. This would explain why washed and refined earth was produced right into the 1940s, being specially prepared for the highest grade of woollens. Nevertheless, washed and refined fuller's earth would not sufficiently clean the special goods made in the Dewsbury district of Yorkshire. Presumably that area preferred earth from Surrey. In the United States, fuller's earth from England was little used for fulling wool.

2. DETERGENTS AND SOAPS

Until more drastic means of cleaning were invented, few households did not possess a packet of this dirty looking powder to use when those troublesome greasy marks appeared on one's clothes. It was a very popular household cleaning agent for a number of years and proved to be ideal for removing finger marks from wallpaper as well as fabrics.

Fuller's earth is still regarded as better than soap or solvents for cleaning heavily oil-soiled textiles, such as dirty car mats. From 1951, fuller's earth granules were produced at Bath for use as an industrial floor cleaning agent, because of its great ability to absorb spilt oil and other materials. It has therefore found use in the cleaning of rugs, carpets, blankets and worsted yarns, and textiles such as woollens, worsted cloths and silk. During the First World War, fuller's earth was sent to Kidderminster where it was used in the carpet industry in that town. After the war, cloth manufacturers as far apart as Galashields in Scotland and Wellington in Somerset were being supplied from Bath.

3. REFINING OF EDIBLE OILS AND FATS

There is a report that, in the late 19th century, fuller's earth was hauled to a small bakery in Holloway in Bath, opposite the end of Calton Road but for what purpose is unknown. In 1868, John Fordred in the United States patented a process for bleaching vegetable oils, paraffin wax and fats using fuller's earth. Two years later, the production of margarine was patented and, by 1891, 'white lard' was being manufactured from American cottonseed!

It was not until 1880 that fuller's earth came to be widely used for refining edible oils, as it had the property of clarifying and deodorising animal and vegetable oils. A Chicago company worked out a process which led to the rapid spread of the procedure throughout the United States. In consequence, there was a high demand for earth from England, as this was cheaper than any being mined in the United States. Untreated English fuller's earth has a very low level of oil retention and the American chemist Charles L. Parsons showed that edible oil could be readily extracted from it by naphtha, carbon tetrachloride and other solvents, while the colouring matter was left behind with the earth.

Parsons was later to encourage the exploitation of the United States' own deposits of earth, so that there would be less reliance on imports. In 1899, there were new discoveries of fuller's earth at Bakersfield in California but it was some time before these deposits were developed. In this country, refining plants for edible oils and fats were being built by 1893 and this would have caused an increase in the sale of earth for the home market. The decolourising and clarifying of vegetable oils had become an important use of fuller's earth.

In 1912, around 75% of the English production of fuller's earth was being shipped to the United States for use in these clarification processes. This dropped to 64% by 1915 and by 1933 very little was still being sent to the USA. The production in England rose dramatically in 1933 and again after the Second World War. At the time of the First World War, Owen Keevil claimed that 75% of the output of the works was being used in food production and that this figure was increasing. In the following years, earth from Tucking Mill was required by manufacturers of foodstuffs such as Pearce & Duff, while Alfred Bird & Sons, makers of custard and baking powder, also bought fuller's earth from there and sold it to druggists all over the United Kingdom.

During the First World War, the Germans found ways of using fuller's earth to make inedible fats consumable! A firm of analytical chemists in Manchester, W.B. Hart, were supplied with regular quantities of fuller's earth from Bath during and after the war. In October 1919, there was a crisis, due to a railway strike, and the correspondence from Hart's records that the earth was *urgent for food purposes*, probably the clarifying of oils and fats. Because of the urgency, two motor vehicles, belonging to Messrs N. Kilvert & Sons of Trafford Park in Manchester, were sent to Combe Hay to collect the required consignment, which was given the code name 'Albine'! The drivers were told that *'Combe Hay was just beyond the three mile stone from Bath and that it has a tall iron chimney'*. Seven tons was despatched in seventy bags in this operation. There were more complaints from Harts in 1923. The Fullers' Earth Union assured Harts that they were always sent *'freshly produced powder'*. The Cooperative Wholesale Society and Hugon & Co. Ltd, who made 'Atora' beef suet, both ordered earth from Bath for the refining of lard.

The decolourising of glycerides, present in animal fats and vegetable oils, is best achieved with a 4-6% moisture content, as it seems that the presence of water is necessary to allow cation exchange to take place. The moisture content of Bath's fuller's earth is 34-36% on a calcite-free basis, so a considerable amount of water had to be removed to make the earth suitable for this market. The product, known as 'Fulmont', was used in suspension for the refining and bleaching of glyceride oils due to its properties of adsorption. It removes both colour and impurities at the same time from fats, oils and similar substances, and therefore contributes to the appetising appearance of margarine, cooking fat and edible oil products. In this country, during World War Two the demand for refined edible fats increased. It has also been used to clear wine, acting as a fining agent, and in the refining of sugar and glucose.

4. THE OIL INDUSTRY

In the latter part of the 19th century, it had been discovered that fuller's earth was also very effective in refining mineral oils. It has been suggested that the reason that Garrett installed a mill at Tucking Mill was because he wanted to get into the oil refining market in the United States. In this context, the milled earth would have been used to filter the oil at some stage in the refining process. During the First World War, 60 tons of earth per week were being despatched to J. Crosfield & Sons of Warrington, chemical manufacturers. It was stated that this was vital for war work.

In 1940, Dr Barbara S. Neumann, a Hungarian research chemist, came to work for the Company at Redhill. She brought knowledge of the processes used for the making of Union Bentonite, which had important uses in the oil industry. This was produced at Combe Hay and named 'Fulbent' in 1946, various mixtures being known as Fulbent 182 and 150. She became a leading authority on the analysis, processing and application of clays, especially montmorillonite, and her work led to the very successful products named Fulmonts.

In the summer of 1941, the Ministry of Supply forecast a demand for Union Bentonite of 10,000 tons per annum and this required an increase from 100 to 250 tons per week to be produced at the Combe Hay works. In the 1950s, with the rapid expansion of the large petroleum refineries in the United Kingdom, there was a growing demand for activated earth for treating lubricating oils. There were regular shipments of earth from Bath to the refineries on Milford Haven and that at Llandarcy, situated some three miles south west of Neath. It is used for the filtering and cleaning of hydrocarbon oils, such as motor oils, to which additives must later be added, and for the regeneration of lubricating oils. The motor-oil product known as 'Filtrate' may possibly have been made in this way. By the 1960s, there was a sharp decline in the demand for 'S' grade earth as new refining techniques came in which did not depend on fuller's earth.

Fuller's earth has also been used extensively in drilling for oil and gas. There was a dramatic increase in export orders for Fulbent from Shell-Mex and the Anglo-Iranian (known as the Anglo-Persian prior to 1936) oil companies in November 1946. In consequence, No. 2 mill had to be run for fourteen hours a day and an extra miner and two other workers were required. Large quantities of earth continued to be supplied from Bath to the refineries in Iran during the 1950s. Later, it was used in the development of the oil and gas fields in the North Sea, as well as being exported to many other places in the world. It has also been used in drilling water wells.

When used for drilling, the earth was mixed with soda ash and water so that the mixture became equivalent to bentonite. This 'sodium-exchanged' swelling clay was the first commercial synthetic bentonite in the United Kingdom, hence its name, Fulbent. As such, it was an important component of the 'mud' used to bring the cuttings to the surface from the drilling bit. It lubricated the drill bit and sealed the walls of the borehole. The mud was pumped down the central bore of the drill where it cooled the drilling bit and then took impurities and debris up the annulus to the surface. At the same time, it formed an impermeable coating which stabilised the sides of the borehole. Its density was critical in order to keep the oil and gas being exploited in position, and to prevent them from mixing.

It is the rheological properties, that is the modification of flow properties

Diagram to demonstrate the use of fuller's earth (drilling 'mud') in drilling.

DRILLING FOR WATER OIL OR GAS

a   **Slurry of fuller's earth and water is pumped down central bore**

b   **Slurry cools drilling bit or cutter**

c   **Slurry carries cutting debris to the surface**

of a fluid medium, which led to it being used in drilling muds. The product was known as 'Fulloid'. It had the power to control viscosity and to carry particles in suspension. Fulloid was also used to give wall support to boreholes due to its thixotropic properties when suspended in water, in other words, if left suspended in a liquid its particles bind themselves into a gel but, if agitated, the bond breaks down and the system reverts to a thick liquid which forms an excellent lubricant.

5. MINER'S POWDER

For a number of years, low grade, ground fuller's earth, known as 'miner's earth', was supplied to pits in South Wales, the Forest of Dean, Bedworth in Warwickshire, and Canterbury, as well as local mines, for damping down the coal dust in underground workings. Ground limestone and slate quarry dust were also used for the same purpose. The earth was dried in the kilns and then ground to produce a fine dust, which Owen Keevil claimed was the only product not injurious to men and animals, being hygienic, antiseptic and not harmful if inhaled. This dusting with fuller's earth reduced the danger of explosions caused by coal dust, as had happened in the North Somerset Coalfield at the Camerton, Conygre and Norton Hill pits.

In April 1920, W.F. Keevil at Redhill pointed out that crushed stone dust was cheaper than fuller's earth for this purpose and that it was not worth the Combe Hay plant supplying this trade any longer. Despite this comment, earth continued to be supplied to the mines and, in March 1929, such was the demand that it required full time work from the men. Much of the miner's powder was transported to the pits for a number of years by the Great Western Railway and other railways.

6. PHARMACEUTICAL USES

For a period of time, fuller's earth was mixed with radioactive spa water at the Royal Mineral Water Hospital for Rheumatic Diseases in Bath, to form a mud-like paste which was used for the treatment of arthritic and rheumatic joints. The mixture provided an effective means of pain relief. The treatment was later abandoned because it induced micturition. After the Second World War, it was also used at the Hospital '*for those soothing mud packs which gentle-fingered nurses delight to plaster on ones aching back at Bath's hydropathic establishments*'. At one stage, the hospital used up to half a ton of mixed fuller's earth and water per day!

By the 1920s, the important pharmaceutical market required the more refined product YB20, produced at Combe Hay. For many years, fuller's earth has been known to give relief in cases of eczema. It may help with weeping eczema because it absorbs the fatty as well as the irritant substances. It has therefore been incorporated in creams and talcs for skin

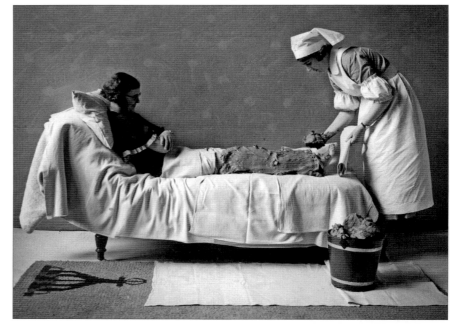

Photograph showing the use made of fuller's earth in Bath at the Royal National Hospital for Rheumatic Diseases (the Mineral Water Hospital).
ROMAN BATHS MUSEUM

High purity Fullers' Earth powders and creams can be purchased in many High Street chemist shops.

Creams and powders based on fuller's earth.
LAPORTE INDUSTRIES LTD

complaints. It was found that, when bandages contained fuller's earth, it promoted rapid healing of lewisite poison gas blisters. Similar healing properties also occurred on blisters caused by mustard gas. Veterinary surgeons have used fuller's earth on horses' hocks and other sores.

Fuller's earth has been included in cosmetics for a number of years. Rouse Brothers of London were supplied with earth from Bath for the toilet powders which they produced. They submitted an order for Special SB Powder. This was prepared from yellow earth from right on the outcrop: *'The powder was prepared by mixing 3.5cwt of yellow, 1cwt of blue and 0.5cwt of china clay on the mill floor. Afterwards it was fed into the mill.'* It was the firm of W. Matthew in London that first put a proprietary brand on the market for toilet and medicinal purposes. Matthew's Fuller's Earth Cream was around by 1900 and was used as an emollient to provide soothing and healing, being applied to different kinds of skin inflammation. Girls in the cotton mills used fuller's earth on their hands and actresses counteracted the grease paint in their make-up with it. It is still used in modern pharmacy and cosmetics in the form of both cream and powder, usually mixed with talc, boric acid, magnesium and zinc oxides, and then perfumed. During the Second World War, it was sold in the NAAFI as a foot powder. YB20 was a careful blend of yellow and blue earths, and after being milled and screened to 200 mesh, which made it very fine, it was used by pharmaceutical suppliers from 1890 until the 1960s. Boots the Chemists, Timothy Whites and British Drug Houses all bought fuller's earth from Bath.

Robertson has pointed out that, for many years, pharmacists had a drawer labelled 'Terr. Fullon', as its medicinal uses had long been recognized. It was not until the British Pharmacopoeia Codex of 1949 that recognition was given to the range of pharmaceutical clays. He goes on to point out that in cases of paraquat poisoning, calcium montmorillonite is considered to be the most effective adsorbent remedy, as it is for any of the bipyridinium compounds. He further commented that the use of fuller's earth to adsorb poisons has been known for centuries yet even today, with its proven effectiveness, it is still not included in some first aid boxes! It was once hawked in the villages of the fen district of East Anglia for filtering peaty drinking water and it has also been used to soften deposits in kettles.

7. FOUNDRY USES

There was a meteoric rise in the production of fuller's earth from 1933 onwards. In that year, a Mr Roland was sent a sample of No. 2 Special earth from some two feet below the 'Black Jack', near the top of the 'All Top' seam. In August, he took a consignment which was definitely stated to be for foundry use. This became the basis for moulding clay. It was named 'Fulbond' in 1934 and consisted of 84% pure sand, 15% fuller's earth and 1% bentonite. In 1941, calcium montmorillonite was called Fulbond No. 1 and clay treated with 4% sodium carbonate (soda ash) was named Fulbond No. 2. Fulbond No. 3, containing less soda ash, was also used by the foundries. With the installation of the Dunford & Elliott rotary louvre dryer around 1942, it meant that these fuller's earth products could be prepared more easily for use in the moulding sands required by the foundries.

In the highly mechanised foundries it is used for bonding and strengthening their moulding sands, so that the sand keeps its moulding power through a series of thermal shocks, as it is used time and again in the castings. Sand and Fulbond mixes are used in both iron and non-ferrous metal foundries. The moistened sand is formed round a pattern by ramming to make the mould. When the pattern is removed, it leaves a cavity of the required shape into which molten metal is poured. The Fulbond gives physical strength to the sand mould and makes it easier to knock out the castings. There was another sharp increase in production after the Second World War due to the expansion in activated earths and the demand for these bonding clays. This reduced the need to import bentonite from the United States.

8. CIVIL ENGINEERING

In large-scale engineering works, specially treated fuller's earth is used to fill the interstices of the foundations for tunnels and dams, for sealing porous strata such as sands or gravels and for stopping water movements.

The rheological properties of fuller's earth also apply to the product Fulbent. It was used by civil engineers for its impermeability and coating properties for soil stabilisation, for grouting to prevent ground water flow, support for trench walls in a technique known as 'diaphragm wall' construction, and for tunnelling and drilling in permeable strata. When Fulbent was used for grouting work, a very small amount was mixed with 30% cement and 70% fly ash.

The twin-tunnel underpass at Hyde Park Corner, built in 1960 between Piccadilly and Knightsbridge in London, was the first time that reinforced concrete diaphragm walling was used in a major civil engineering structure in the United Kingdom. Some years later, the same method was used in the construction of the Royal Portbury Dock near Bristol.

For the London project, the fuller's earth in the form of Fulbent, *i.e.* bentonite, was obtained from Laporte's workings in Redhill in Surrey. The method involved digging a trench, which was then stabilised with a slurry of Fulbent, before inserting steel reinforcing cages. When the concrete replaced the Fulbent, the result was a reinforced concrete wall. These formed the retaining walls of the underpass and excavation of the carriageways could proceed.

Fulbent is ideal for this kind of construction for a number of reasons. First, it can be transported dry in bulk tankers, stored in silos on site and mixed with water when required. Second, due to its high density it forms a physical barrier preventing the sides of the excavation from falling in. Third, when mixed with water, it increases in viscosity with the passage of time, if it is undisturbed. It forms a very thin film on

Diagram showing the construction of reinforced concrete diaphragm walls using fuller's earth.

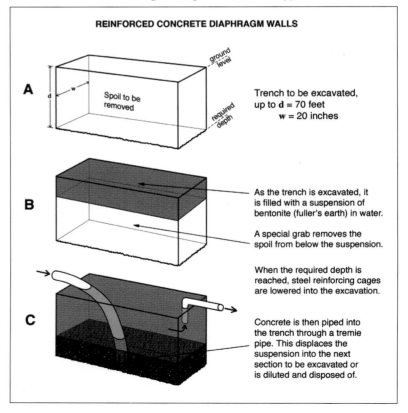

REINFORCED CONCRETE DIAPHRAGM WALLS

A — Spoil to be removed — ground level — required depth — d, w

Trench to be excavated, up to **d** = 70 feet
w = 20 inches

B

As the trench is excavated, it is filled with a suspension of bentonite (fuller's earth) in water.

A special grab removes the spoil from below the suspension.

When the required depth is reached, steel reinforcing cages are lowered into the excavation.

C

Concrete is then piped into the trench through a tremie pipe. This displaces the suspension into the next section to be excavated or is diluted and disposed of.

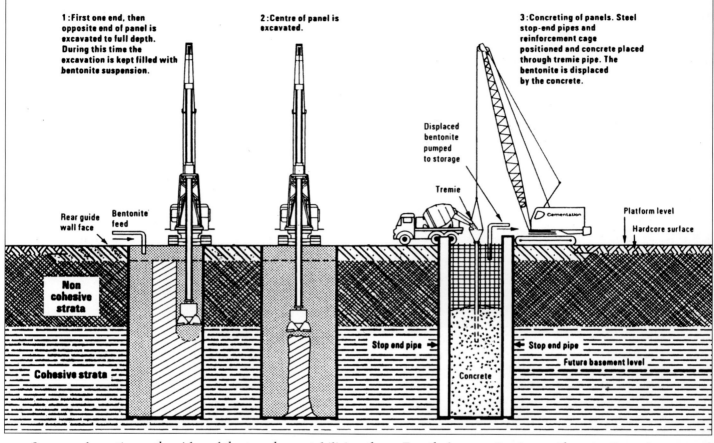

1 : First one end, then opposite end of panel is excavated to full depth. During this time the excavation is kept filled with bentonite suspension.

2 : Centre of panel is excavated.

3 : Concreting of panels. Steel stop-end pipes and reinforcement cage positioned and concrete placed through tremie pipe. The bentonite is displaced by the concrete.

Displaced bentonite pumped to storage

Tremie

Rear guide wall face

Bentonite feed

Platform level

Hardcore surface

Non cohesive strata

Cohesive strata

Stop end pipe

Stop end pipe

Future basement level

Concrete

Sequence of operations using fuller's earth in diaphragm walling. CEMENTATION PILING & FOUNDATIONS LTD

the sides of the trench, so stabilising them. Fourth, because it mixes with water it can be pumped into the excavation. Finally, when finished with and greatly diluted, it can be disposed of through the public sewers.

9. CARRIERS AND BINDERS

The high surface area of the calcium montmorillonite molecule, as explained in an earlier chapter, led to it being used in the granular state as a carrier or medium for insecticides and fungicides. Fuller's earth granules, which have been dried, are water stable and have therefore been used as a carrier for pesticides and herbicides. They provided a safe and harmless method of agricultural crop protection, because chemically they are non-toxic and in pellet form there is no dust to cause a hazard. Pesticides have used fuller's earth together with nicotine or sulphur dust. They have the advantage that they give uniform dispersion of the toxicant, which helps the plant to retain the pesticide in wind and rain, as well as maintaining the toxicity of the product. The pesticide chlordimeform is very strongly adsorbed by fuller's earth and is not easily removed by water. It has also been used as a carrier for copper chloride in the refining process of kerosene. Finely milled fuller's earth powders have been used as fillers. 'All Top', known as AT, was described as being *'rough stuff'* and years ago it was used as a carrier for the insecticide Derris dust. The upper part of the seam at Combe Hay, in which there is the higher concentration of calcite, was dried to a 3% moisture content and then sold as a carrier for fertilisers, such as the widely used 'National Growmore'.

It has also been used as a binder in cattle feed for the reasons mentioned above. Another form of Fulbent, used in animal feed pellets, bonds the rather dry ingredients together and also acts as a lubricant and so may help the animals to ingest the feed. By far the largest use of granules has been for animal litter, introduced in 1959. This developed into the cat litter product which was produced in very large quantities, due to its power to highly absorb both moisture and odour. It was despatched to Armitages in Nottingham. Sadly, the cat litter plant was fitted out with new equipment just two years before the works were finally closed.

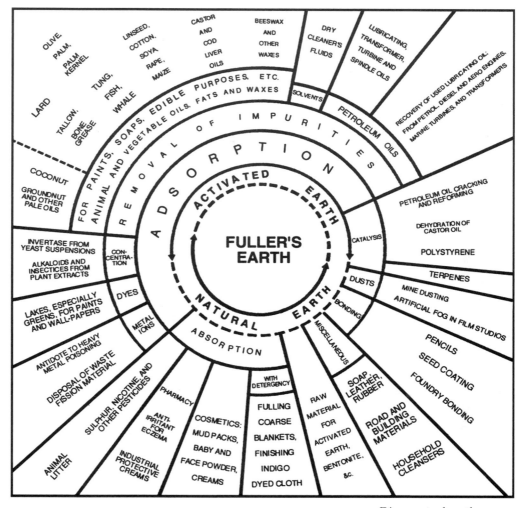

Diagram to show the many uses of fuller's earth
AFTER R.H.S. ROBERTSON

10. SOME OF THE MANY OTHER USES

In some chemical processes fuller's earth is used as a catalyst, holding the molecules of several substances sufficiently close together for them to react upon each other. It is also used as a carrier for other chemicals, and its use as a base for sticky insecticides and for other substances which must be held in a manageable form until required for use.

Fuller's earth has had something like one hundred different uses, including the production of paints, polishes, pottery glazes and in pencils, in which it is mixed with graphite to form the 'lead'. More than one person has speculated as to whether there was any link between fuller's earth and Plasticine, which was developed by Wm Harbutt, ARCA, in 1897 and produced by 1900 at Bathampton, on the eastern outskirts of Bath. As Harbutts kept the ingredients of their product secret, it is possible that they could have purchased fuller's earth through an intermediary.

A WORLD WIDE MARKET: CUSTOMERS AT HOME AND ABROAD
1915-1929

During the First World War and the years following, customers included the CWS Lard Refinery at West Hartlepool, which complained that six tons of earth had arrived in a wet condition because it had been sent in an open railway wagon. J.L. Cardwell of Manchester, who were manufacturers of colours, chemicals and minerals, bought fuller's earth from Bath. Other customers about that time were various woollen mills in Yorkshire, as well as Isaac Carr & Co. at Twerton Mills in Bath. Black Clay was ordered by D.L. Howe and M. Langland & Sons during the First World War and, in the early 1930s, by Francis Stevenson, dyers in Dundee. At Combe Hay, they were grinding Black Clay which required coal to make up a load of 30 tons. Its exact nature and use are unknown.

Some of the companies being supplied from Bath in 1918 were Shaw Haigh at Puckleden Mills, Holmfirth; Grove Dye Works, Leeds; The Strathclyde Paint Co., Glasgow (supplied by Sloan's steamer from Bristol); Marling & Co's mills at Stroud; Fox Bros, Wellington, Somerset; William Watson & Co. Forebank Dye Works, Dundee; Messrs Sir Titus Salt, Bart, Sons & Co. Ltd, Saltaire, Shipley, Yorkshire; and William Beaumont Hart, Manchester Laboratory.

In January 1920, fuller's earth was sent to William Haigh at Holmfirth in Yorkshire. He was an agent for the Fullers' Earth Union and probably arranged deliveries to local woollen mills. He was the recipient of an apologetic and explanatory letter from Keevil about this time, concerning the late delivery of a consignment of fuller's earth from Tucking Mill. The agents of the company in the United States were L.A. Salomon & Brother. They pointed out, at the end of the First World War, that there was increasing competition from American earths and that this accounted for the reduction in the number of orders from the States. Nevertheless, they were still able to get orders for Bath. The Greenwich Lemonade Co., the Olympia Oil & Cake Co. Ltd, Hugon & Co., the makers of 'Atora' beef suet, and J.J. Coleman of Norwich, famous as the makers of mustard powder, were all supplied from Bath. The Cooperative Wholesale Society Soap Works at Irlam, near Manchester, were also customers at that time, while Cussons Sons & Co. Ltd ordered two tons of the finest toilet fuller's earth in 1926. In the same year, Harbutts of Bathampton, the makers of Plasticine, requested samples of powdered fuller's earth and also washed and refined earth!

RIGHT: Photograph taken in 1903 of William Harbutt modelling in Plasticine, which he invented in 1897 and manufactured in Bathampton.
P.J.C. HARBUTT ESQR

FAR RIGHT: A Packet of Harbutt's Plasticine.

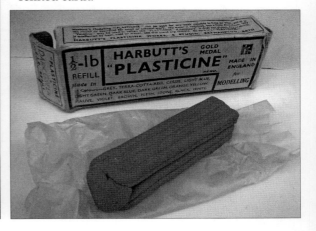

In the 1920s, collieries started ordering fuller's earth for dusting in the roadways of the pits to prevent explosions due to coal dust. After two years of research, in 1926, the Fullers' Earth Union succeeded in producing an earth likely to meet the needs of the Anglo-Persian Oil Co. in connection with refining mineral oil. The result was an order for 150 tons a month to be taken by the Great Western Railway to Llandarcy. The company was based at Port Skewen in Swansea. National Oil Refineries at Llandarcy were to become customers in the 1930s. The records show that earth was shipped to the United States and Europe from the docks in Bristol, and Germany imported earth until the outbreak of the First World War. It was there, on 17th November 1909, that clay was activated with acid for the first time. This treatment was not repeated in the United Kingdom until 1928, when it was tried at the Company's works at Redhill in Surrey. It should be noted that fuller's earth from Bath was unsuitable for this process and it was not used at any of the plants in the area.

The Australian Woollen Mills in Sydney was supplied with twenty tons of screened blue lump in 1921. The following year, there was an order from the Globe Worsted Mills at Marrickville in New South Wales. The Army & Navy Cooperative Society ordered fuller's earth for its store in Bombay in 1926. Another shipment to Australia in 1927 was to a firm of manufacturing chemists, who made Solyptol soap and distilled eucalyptus oil. The same year, eighteen bags of washed and refined lump was sent to the Kaipoi Woollen Manufacturing Co. in New Zealand. The Fullers' Earth Union publicised its products at the Oil, Chemical & Colour Trades Exhibition in the 1920s and this resulted in many enquiries for samples. Other customers who were supplied from Combe Hay in the mid 1920s included John Brooke & Sons, Berry Burn, Huddersfield; British Oil & Cake Mills, Rochester; Allen & Hanburys, Hull; Joseph Crossfield, Warrington; J.C. Davey & Co. Bitton; and Rouse Bros, London WI.

1930-1939

In the next decade, the customers included the Boots Pure Drug Co., Imperial Chemical Industries at Widnes and the Frazene Paint & Varnish Co. in Fulham. Abbey Mills in Morpeth, Northumberland wanted half a ton of fuller's earth *'suitable for scouring blankets'*. There were also more local customers, such as J.C. Dovey of the Golden Valley Mills at Bitton, between Bath and Bristol, who wanted samples of blue, drab and Somerset super fine powders in 1934. In 1938, John Hatton, Spa Director of the hot springs in Bath, visited the works and wrote afterwards *'As we use so much fuller's earth here in our treatments, I was very pleased to have all the information you gave me at first hand and to have the opportunity of seeing the running of the whole process'*. He is recorded as having ordered six tons of fuller's earth for the Mud Bath Department in May 1936!

The product known as Special Somerset No. 2 was mined from the extreme top of the seam, just below the 'Black Jack', which was ground from the coarsest and sandiest earth. This product was wanted by the Universal Grinding Wheel Company in Stafford for metal moulding. National Oil Refineries increased their order in July 1934 to twenty tons per week for blended earth, which was known as SH10Y, being a blend of SH33 and SH50. This meant that more Union Z was required from Germany. The Shell-Mex and British Petroleum oil companies were using SH50 by November 1934. The following year, Lobitos Oilfields Ltd of Ellesmere Port in Cheshire became a customer for SH33. In 1934, customers in the British Colonies wanted 200 mesh Blue Powder as a carrier for insecticides, which were then being sprayed by air.

By the autumn of 1938, Owen Keevil was lamenting the depressed state of trade from Bath. There had been a decline in orders from the United States, where American earth was now cheaper. Orders from Yorkshire were down. Keevil wrote '*unfortunately the fashion has changed, fancy suitings are now largely worn to the neglect of the navy blue and dark cloths of former days and fancy suitings do not require Fuller's Earth for finishing*'. Allen & Hanbury's wanted a consignment for their branch in Shanghai in 1939 and Price's Patent Candle Co. Ltd was another customer. At the Somerset Week Exhibition in April 1932, the Fullers' Earth Union displayed samples of blue lump, yellow lump, SP4 powder, YB4 powder, Washed & Refined lump, and Miner's powder.

1940-1949

During the Second World War, no margarine factory could function without fuller's earth and it was used for manufacturing other foods in contracts for the Government. Lubricating oils for the army and navy also required supplies.

Throughout the 1940s, a great number of companies received fuller's earth products from Bath. These included the Midland Motor Cylinder Co. in Smethwick, which ordered Fulbond No. 2, the English Steel Corporation in Sheffield and the Bristol Aeroplane Co. Engine Division at Filton, both of which took Fulbond No. 1. The foundries of the Ford Motor Co. used Union Bentonite. For drilling purposes, D'Arcy Exploration requested Union Bentonite No. 1 when drilling near Lulworth in Dorset and Bremner Well Drilling Co. wanted Fulbent 150 for their work at Saltburn in Yorkshire. Imperial Chemical Industries Ltd and Hoover Ltd placed a large order for 'All Top' to be used for oil absorption on the workshop floors. 'All Top' was also supplied to Bengers Ltd in Northern Ireland. Other customers were Rowney & Co., Winsor & Newton Ltd and the Cumberland Pencil Co., which used Fulbent as a bonding agent for holding together the particles of graphite, so making the lead of pencils smooth and consistent in quality. Other companies using fuller's earth products in the manufacture of paints and varnishes included the Torbay Paint Company and Mander Brothers at Wolverhampton.

Customers who were supplied in 1944 included ICI and Thos Firth & John Brown, whilst in November 1946, there was a dramatic increase in orders for Fulbent from oil companies in the Middle East, including Anglo-Iranian, the Kuwait Oil Co., the Iraq Petroleum Co., the Anglo-American Oil Co. and the Shell Oil Co. The next year, there were supplies to Dartmouth Auto Castings, Westinghouse Brakes, English Electric, Cape Asbestos, Ferranti and Murphy Chemical Co., with requests for samples of Fulbond from foundries in the United Kingdom as well as China and India.

1950-1979

The main outlets for the earth from Combe Hay during this period were to the motor trade for foundry moulding sands, the agricultural industries for fertilisers and cattle feed additives, and the pet litter and cosmetic markets. Many of the previously mentioned customers continued during this period. In addition, an order was received in March 1951 from Swift & Co. in Australia, manufacturers of canned meat, and Van den Berghs, makers of margarine. The Union Oil & Cake Mills would have used the earth in producing cattle feeds. Most of the yellow earth was used by Timothy Whites the Chemists and other loads were despatched to the United States, where L.A. Salomon & Brother had been the main agents of the Fullers' Earth Union since 1919. In October 1931, they had placed an order for fifty tons of FP powder, which was a mixture of Best and 'All Top' earth. This outlet was to continue for a number of years despite the severe competition. Salomons always insisted on their order being despatched in new twill sacks with their logo on them. This was in the form of a diamond with an 'S' inside. Other sacks had 'WK' and 'OK' 14 or 20 on them, references to the managers Walter and Owen Keevil. Twill or hessian was replaced by paper in the 1950s. One of these products was known as OK140. From 1951, Qualcast, famous for their lawnmowers, were using some 2,000 tons per year but this may have been largely bentonite which was imported from Greece. Between 1974 and 1980, however, there was a fall due to the oil crisis.

When Keelings were transporting the fuller's earth, some 150 tons were leaving the works every day and much of this was for cat litter, being sent to Armitage's in Nottingham. Other customers were Fison's, producers of fertilisers, at Avonmouth and Immingham, the Burmidge Aluminium Works in West Bromwich, Brockhouse Castings in Wolverhampton and the steel makers Dunlop & Rankin. Other companies included Ideal Standard in Hull and Cape Asbestos at Workington, the Boots Pure Drug Co., which had YB20 sent in sacks, and British Petroleum at Llandarcy, which used bentonite and later Fulbent for oil refining. William Butler & Co., oil recovery agents, used fuller's earth for recovering lubricating oil. Saltaire in Yorkshire and Foxes Woollen Mill at Wellington in Somerset received smaller amounts of earth.

Just over a year before the plant closed, the manager, H. Beech, stated that standard tonnage was 25,000 tons per annum and was then being sold mainly for foundry bonding sand, fertiliser coating and for cattle food binding. Granules were prepared for the cat litter trade. He went on to point out that to sell this tonnage it was necessary to mine some 30,000 tons, as when it was mined, it contained 28% moisture and that this had to be reduced to between 4% and 8% depending on the product.

NOTES ON CHAPTER 11

For details about the different products see Appendix 2.

Bentonite: Fuller's earth, as found in the South of England, has been replaced by a clay with similar properties known as bentonite.

Bipyridinium: Compounds derived from pyridine C_5H_5N.

Carrier: A substance which assists a chemical reaction, by combining with part or all of the molecule of one of the reacting substances, to form a compound which is then easily decomposed again by the other reacting substance. The carrier is left unchanged. (*A Dictionary of Science,* Penguin)

Chlordimeform: According to Robertson, this pesticide is very strongly adsorbed by fuller's earth and is not easily eluted, *i.e.* removed by washing. It was first produced in 1966 and used on cotton crops in California. It has probably been replaced by more recent pesticides.

Derris dust: An insecticide produced from the roots of any plant of a tropical genus related to peas and beans.

Kerseymere: A twilled cloth of very fine wool. Kersey – a coarse woollen cloth, perhaps named after the village of that name in Suffolk.

Lewisite: Chlorovinyl dichlorarsine, a derivative of arsenic, an oily liquid that causes blistering and other irritation and was used in warfare as a poisonous gas. It is named after W.L. Lewis, an American chemist. (*A Dictionary of Science,* Penguin)

Mordant: Any substance which combines with and fixes a dyestuff in material that cannot be dyed direct. The substance is first impregnated with the mordant. The dye then reacts chemically with the mordant forming an insoluble *lake* which is firmly attached to the fabric. (*A Dictionary of Science,* Penguin)

Mustard gas: Dichlorodiethyl sulphide, the vapour from an oily blistering liquid used in chemical warfare. (*A Dictionary of Science,* Penguin)

NAAFI: Navy, Army & Air Force Institute, an organisation which provided canteens for service personnel.

Paraquat: Is an isomer of Dipyridil (or Bipyridil), two pyridine rings connected by their carbon atoms. It is a powerful herbicide.

Rheology: The science of the deformation and flow of matter.

The **Anglo-Persian Oil Company** was set up in 1912 by the British Government, as a result of the Royal Commission on Fuel Oil for the British Navy. The Government had the controlling interest. In 1934, the name of Persia was changed to Iran, so the name of the company was then changed to the Anglo-Iranian Oil Company.

German green earth was imported for use by oil and paint manufacturers in the 1920s. The Fullers' Earth Union had a factory called Gewerschaft Tannenberg at Magdeburg, with which products were exchanged. During the 1930s, German earth was imported from Hamburg via Bristol Docks on a weekly basis for blending with Somerset earth. For example, SHI0 contained 10% of German activated earth, known as Union Z. O.F. Keevil wrote in 1934 *'while Union Z improves the primary bleach it increases the tendency of the oil to revert after bleaching. This is due to the increased acidity of the blend. The idea of using All Top* [from the Bath mine] *is to counteract acidity by using an earth on the natural side which contains more carbonates or alkali.'*

Athough it was claimed that fuller's earth is non-toxic, several workers suffered from asthma and other chest illnesses. The installation of an efficient dust plant was therefore essential, in addition to respirators being worn when blending the different powders.

Production statistics: The only figures available for the annual output from the Bath area are for 1882-1920. During this period, they varied from 1,000 to 5,000 tons according to demand, with an average between 3,500 and 4,000 tons.

BIBLIOGRAPHY

Sundry booklets produced by Laporte Industries Ltd on different aspects of the industry including:
Fullers' Earth, The Mineral and its Uses, no date
Fullers' Earth, July 1978
Fullers' Earth Products, May 1987
Laporte Earths, no date
Rolls, R., *The Hospital of the Nation,* 1988
Smith, J. Lindsay, 'Non-Stop at Hyde Park'. Article for contractors Cubitts-Fitzpatrick-Shand, 1960-2.

Winter view of the Combe Hay Works in full operation.
SAM FARR/BATH EVENING CHRONICLE

⊰ Chapter 12 ⊱

THE END OF AN ERA

The End of the Industry and the Future

It is now twenty-eight years since the mining and processing of fuller's earth ceased in the Bath area. The Combe Hay mine closed on 29th February 1980, bringing to an end almost one hundred years of the industry in the district. Before closure, 30-35,000 tons of wet earth were being extracted each year, producing 20,000 tons of finished product. The Fullers' Earth Union had been created to bring an end to crippling competition between the small mining companies and finally Laporte Industries Ltd closed the works because it was no longer economical to mine the earth.

According to the report *Mineral Working in Avon – Local Plan, The Consultation Draft*, July 1987, prepared by Interfoss Associates, the reserves of fuller's earth were believed to be sufficient for several years production and the sub-economic resources in the vicinity of the mine at Odd Down were believed to be considerable. It pointed out that the national demand for fuller's earth was slowly increasing, new uses were always being developed and that there could still be an increase in demand in the future for the lower quality material from the Bath area. At that time, planning permission for a total of 318 acres (129 ha) had been given, of which 227 acres (92 ha) were under the control of Laporte Industries Ltd and these were all concentrated round the mine area. The company retained 200 acres (81ha) south of Bath. The report, which was adopted in 1993, indicated that the possibility of future extraction in the local area should be maintained. The mining and processing would not be in the same areas as when last in operation.

Combe Hay Works. A late view of Combe Hay Works in operation, with a loaded and sheeted flatbed lorry visible in the centre.
LAPORTE INDUSTRIES LTD

For a number of years the plant was kept, perhaps in the hope that there would be an upturn in the economic climate but eventually the machinery was scrapped. In July 1984, John Stevens of Chilcompton and others, dismantled all the machinery in the fuller's earth works at Combe Hay. According to David Pollard, who was present, not everything was broken up. Some machines, motors, gear motors, reinforced steel joists and ducting were salvaged. Laporte Industries Ltd sold the remaining part of the site in May 1999. Part of it was redeveloped a few years ago by the local council, Bath & North East Somerset, to provide the Odd Down Park & Ride facility. This might be extended in future if there is the demand. Few motorists, who park their cars there and ride into Bath, realise what happened beneath the surface for so many years!

Today, the works present a sad sight with the buildings becoming more and more dilapidated and the silos streaked with rust. After the site was sold, attempts were made to find new uses for some of the buildings and redevelop the site. At the present time, the site is

being used to recycle topsoil and aggregates.

It is a different story at Tucking Mill, where the reservoir, which completely obliterated the fuller's earth works there, now provides recreation for disabled anglers. The whole area has an air of tranquillity and charm of which William Smith would have approved.

BIBLIOGRAPHY

Moorcock, B.S., & Highley, D.E., *An appraisal of Fuller's Earth resources in England and Wales,* British Geological Survey Technical Report WA/91/75, 1991
Brown, C.J., 'A Geotechnical Study of abandoned mineworkings in the Bath Area', Unpublished PhD. thesis, University of Bristol, 1991
Articles on closure of the mine *Bristol Evening Post,* 17th January 1980, and *Bath Chronicle,* 29th February 1980
Mineral Working in Avon – Local Plan, The Consultation Draft, July 1987, prepared by Interfoss Associates
Mineral Working in Avon – Local Plan, adopted 1993

ABOVE: Tucking Mill House and the Reservoir. 'O Tucking Mill I love thee still', a photograph which portrays the tranquillity of the area today, so much loved by William Smith in his day. The storage lake, which holds 15 million litres of water pumped from the River Avon, was constructed by Wessex Water and completed in 1980. In 1981, the Year of the Disabled, fishing platforms were installed to provide recreation for disabled anglers.
TONY BROWN

RIGHT: The Park & Ride Area showing underground workings. This map, prepared for the enquiry that preceded the construction of the Park & Ride facility to the south of Bath, is a useful indicator of the dates and different methods of extraction in the area which was to be developed.
GCP ARCHITECTS, AUG. 2002
(In colour inside front cover)

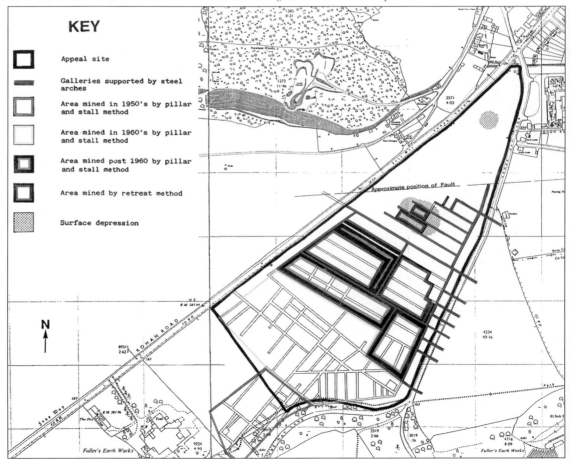

KEY

☐   Appeal site

▬   Galleries supported by steel arches

☐   Area mined in 1950's by pillar and stall method

☐   Area mined in 1960's by pillar and stall method

☐   Area mined post 1960 by pillar and stall method

☐   Area mined by retreat method

▦   Surface depression

N

Henry Newson Garrett at Bath. Taken c.1890 at the W.G. Lewis Art Studios in Seymour Street, Bath. This photograph probably once belonged to his youngest daughter Faith Mary (1877-1963) and later her grandson Peter Goodwyn.
PETER GOODWYN

⊰ Appendix 1 ⊱
BIOGRAPHICAL NOTES
Notes on some of those who worked in the Fuller's Earth Industry

EARLY PIONEERS

James Cawley (1822-1882) was in the fuller's earth business in Surrey before 1851. In that year, his company won a medal at the Great Exhibition in London. A company known as Cawley & Co. Ltd was established around 1886.

Claude William Cawley, James Cawley's son, issued a Prospectus in April 1886 for a limited company. By the following year, he had bought up the small mines at Wellow and at Evergreen on Rush Hill, Odd Down. These eventually became part of the Fullers' Earth Union Ltd on its formation in March 1890, together with the small company at Hodshill in Southstoke. Both the *Bath Herald* and *Bath Journal* of 22nd March 1890 refer to the formation of the Fullers' Earth Union Ltd. Cawley was the first managing director of the new company. He was removed from this position by June 1892 and prevented from trading as a fuller's earth merchant by the following year. He died in 1908.

George Dames was the first secretary of the Company which purchased '*beds of earth at Midford*' from him in February 1890. George and his brother Charles Dames were responsible for the patenting and installation of the equipment for purifying fuller's earth at Midford in 1883. In 1891, George left the Fullers' Earth Union and, with others, formed the Fuller's Earth Mining Company Ltd, at Woburn Sands in Bedfordshire early in that year. One of the partners, named Riley, bought fuller's earth from Midford works, where he was in touch with H.N. Garrett, the new owner at Midford. The company at Woburn Sands only lasted until 1896. He died in 1899 and his brother Charles R. Dames, born in 1849, died on 2nd February 1933 in Tenby.

Henry Newson Garrett was born at Leiston in Suffolk on 6th July 1841, one of the sons of Richard Garrett of the engineering works in that town. He married Mary Susannah Goodwyn (1843-1900) at Covehithe, Suffolk on 6th August 1863. When Richard died in 1866, his three sons, Richard, Henry and Frank, inherited the works but Henry was removed from the company because of his immoral conduct in 1878. He moved to Bath that year with his family and bought a large house at 101 Sydney Place, where he was to live until his death. Sadly, his behaviour contributed to the death of his own son, Alec Henry, born 1879, who committed suicide in the spring of 1907. For a short time, Alec had been the manager at Tucking Mill. Henry Newson died on 13th October 1912 being described as '*manager of a fuller's earth works*'. When the fuller's earth works at Wellow closed in 1894-95, Garrett, who had been part-time manager at Tucking Mill, began the improvement of the works there, introducing more elaborate plant.

Uriah Handley was in charge of the operation at Hodshill to the south of the village of Southstoke in the 1880s. This was known as the Minerals & Mining Company. His brother W.H. Handley was the actual owner, as it was he who sold out to the new Fullers' Earth Union Ltd in February 1890. He was a draper and this would explain the legend that when the first mining was successful, he gave dress material to the women in the village!

Walter Alan Sheppard was in charge at various sites in the early years of the industry. Sheppard was a quarrymaster, living at Evergreen Cottage on Rush Hill in 1884-85, where a stone is engraved with the letters 'W.A.S. 1885', but by 1888, he had become proprietor of a fuller's earth works. It could be that he first exploited the Oolitic building stone on the Evergreen site and then had access to the seam of fuller's earth that lay below. Sheppard then moved to 2 Bloomfield Crescent, the terrace in which William Smith had lived for a time, before moving again to Cleeve House, Midford around 1890 or 1891, when he was in charge of the works at Tucking Mill. By 1899 he was listed as a stone merchant, traction engine and steam roller proprietor. In the 1920s, he served as a Councillor for Bath and ran the local road construction firm of Roadite Ltd, Traction Engine & Road Rolling Contractors, from offices at 22 Milsom Street. He died in 1952 when in his nineties.

William Hamlen of Midford started about 1898, first as a general haulier and later also a coal merchant. With his sons, he was employed to transport fuller's earth from Combe Hay to Top Works and also to take the finished product from Tucking Mill to Midford goods yard. They had a large number of horses and both two and four wheeled carts. The photograph of the horses and cart at Tucking Mill shows Bill, one of the sons. The horses were eventually disposed of around 1935. Hamlen's work for the fuller's earth industry was taken over by John Keeling & Son in the mid 1950s. Hamlens ceased trading about 1967. The father was also the Midford postman at one time and the family had a farm in Limpley Stoke Lane, which they worked until 1920. Another son named Tom was known as 'Rattler'. He was the pump-man at the Combe Down Water Works, behind the works at Tucking Mill.

MANAGERS

Walter Frank Keevil may have been one of the founding members of the Fullers' Earth Union. Keevil joined one of the Somerset companies in 1883 and was manager at Wellow and Combe Hay, probably appointed about 1889 or 1891. It is uncertain when he left Bath. Some sources give 1893, when he was listed as the agent at Park fuller's earth mine in Surrey, which closed the following year. Copyhold fuller's earth works was also said to have been worked by Keevil for the Fullers' Earth Union about this time. This is unlikely as he was still in charge at Combe Hay in 1912, before moving to Redhill, where he was manager until 1927. He is listed at various addresses in Bath; Midland Terrace (1888), Winchester Road (1892-3), Bloomfield Place (1900) and at Beechen Cliff House in 1904. By 1933, he was an Advisory Director to the Company, eventually giving 51 years service to the industry. He died on 24th February 1934. It seems likely that the Keevils may have been a Bath family, as after Keevil left the area, he was always interested in news from Bath.

Owen F. Keevil, the son of W.F. Keevil, entered the fuller's earth business in 1898, joining the Union the following year. He was at Combe Hay, as assistant manager, in 1912, living in Shakespeare Avenue and by September 1913 was in charge at Bath. He spent some time in the USA at Klondyke in Arkansas, where the Union had deposits of fuller's earth. This was for a period of ten months from October 1913 to July 1914, during which time a Mr Dyer was in charge at Combe Hay. He was certainly back in Bath before the Fullers' Earth Union took over the Tucking Mill or Midford Works in 1915 and by July 1922, was living at Alexandra Park Gardens. He was living at 'The Limes' on Wellsway before moving to Redhill in June 1927. When he became manager in Bath he was in correspondence, almost daily, with his father in Redhill and it is from these records that much early information has been gained. His wife may have been German.

R.W. Nicholds was born in 1900. He served in the British Army from 1917 to 1919 and, on his discharge, with the rank of Second Lieutenant, Owen Keevil wanted him at Combe Hay as a shorthand typist – previously he had worked for the Bath Gas Light & Coke Company. In 1927, he succeeded Keevil as manager at Combe Hay. He had the Firs Cottages next to the works, built after the First World War, and lived in one of them. He moved to Redhill in 1937, where he succeeded Owen Keevil in the early months of 1941. Eventually, around 1947, he was the Chairman of the Fullers' Earth Union. He finally retired in 1965 after nearly 40 years of service in the industry.

C.H. Pittman was clerk to Nicholds, until he became Works Manager at Combe Hay in 1937. He left in February 1940, possibly on war service.

Jack T. Smith was taken on as a shorthand typist at the age of 21 in April 1936 to assist Pittman. Later, he worked for a time at Redhill, before returning to Bath as Manager from 1940 to 1943, when he was called up and joined the Royal Navy in the Second World War. He returned to Redhill after the war.

Tom W. Holmes arrived in Bath on 12th May 1943 from Redhill, as deputy to Smith and was then manager until he retired in 1959 or 1960. He lived in No. 2 The Firs, the more southerly of the two cottages. During his time, he oversaw a great expansion in the works and production. He died about 1978.

C.F. Lloyd-Jones became manager in Bath on the retirement of Mr Holmes and held that position until 1967.

Horace Beech began as deputy manager in October 1966 and was manager from November 1967 to 1979. He had previously been in the coal industry.

Derek Oliver was manager for the final months of the works at Combe Hay and on closure went to Redhill.

Douglas Anthony came to Bath around 1967 from Laportes at Luton and was the deputy mine manager in the last years of operation, before going to Redhill when the plant closed.

OTHERS

J.S. Highfield, a consulting engineer with the firm Highfield & Roger Smith, he was one of the Directors of the Fullers' Earth Union along with Simpson and Gray. He was Chairman in the 1930s and died suddenly in August 1945.

Charles L. Parsons (1867-1954) was a chemist with the US government. Around 1911, he encouraged the home production of fuller's earth and, in consequence, there was a fall in the demand for earth from England.

Barbara S. Neumann née Beer, later Mrs Emodi, came from Hungary in 1940. As a Research Chemist, Dr Neumann became a leading authority on the analysis, processing and application of montmorillonites. Her work led to the highly successful Fulmont products. She continued to work for the Company into the 1960s.

Mark Barrett was the blacksmith at the smithy across the road from the Cross Keys Inn on Midford Road until it closed just before the Second World War. He married Clara Clifford from Southstoke and was often employed by the Fullers' Earth Union on a number of jobs.

SOME EMPLOYEES

Cyril Banks worked at Odd Down.

L.J. Banks was a fitter.

Frank Bennett from Larkhall was aged 28 in 1918 and drove a steam waggon. He was exempted from military service in October 1916.

W. Biggs was a blender during the 1930s.

Charles Brinkworth worked at Tucking Mill but was killed in the First World War about 1917.

L. Brinkworth was an electrician in February 1947.

Sidney Brinkworth milled the fuller's earth at Tucking Mill in the early years of the 20th century. Alec Palmer, the son of the foreman, remembered that he looked like a flour miller because he was always covered with dust! He left when milling stopped there at the beginning of the 1920s.

Frank Boddy worked on the kilns at both Combe Hay and Tucking Mill. According to his daughter, Florrie Parham, in 1918 Frank was working 8$^1/_2$ hours on the kilns and at the same time hauling coke and bringing back the kiln doors at the time when they were being reconstructed. He worked with a man called Griffin. He went on the steam lorry into Bath and also used a pony and cart to go to Tucking Mill. The records show that he was working 22$^1/_2$ hours on the kiln and also hauling brick and 'muck' *i.e.* waste. He fetched kiln plates from Midford and worked with Dobson the builder on the reconstruction of the kilns at Combe Hay. When he worked for 44$^1/_2$ hours on the kilns, he was paid the handsome sum of £1.18.11d, just under £2! For a time, Frank Boddy also worked on the open cast site at the Duchy. By the autumn of 1932 he was seriously ill in the Mineral Hospital. He lived at Woodside Cottages in Odd Down and was 37 in 1918. He retired in the 1950s.

Frank Busson, from Hinton Charterhouse, started as a miner around 1936-37 and by 1943 was pit foreman. He was hurt in a roof fall in January 1945. He worked in the industry for 23 years, retiring in the early 1960s.

Barry Butt was a process worker.

Nathan Chappell was employed at Tucking Mill in the early years of the 20th century to mend sacks.

R. Cleaves is listed in 1918, aged 50, as a watchman, sawyer and handyman. He lived at Hawthorn Grove, Combe Down.

James Coleman was employed at the Top Works during the First World War.

Bill Coles was a miner in the final years.

Jack Coles assisted Ern West and lived at Tucking Mill Cottage in the 1930s.

Eric Collins was a miner at the Grove in 1968.

George Collins was a miner and was injured underground in a fall of Top Earth. He was father of Eric, John and Roy.

John Collins was a miner and lorry driver.

Roy Collins worked in the last adit along with Roy Straffen and 'Bunny' Rabbits and Jenkins during the final years of the industry in Bath.

Frank Cox was the mine foreman in the final years, having worked for the company for nearly 25 years.

Eddie Croker was born at Southstoke and after war service was taken on as a miner in August 1947. Following an accident that left him disabled, he was the winchman at Combe Hay. Later, he worked outside the new mine at Southstoke until closure. He lived in William Smith's house at Tucking Mill from about 1954, when he succeeded Ern West as caretaker at that site.

H. Doug. Dainton, son of William Dainton, was taken on at the end of 1946 to work in the factory.

William Dainton worked for the Union from 1917 until 1932. He had started at the age of 16.

E. Ted Densley, son of Sam Densley, was reinstated in December 1946 having previously worked for the Company before being called up for war service. When tarring the roof at the Pan after the Second World War, he fell off and broke his arm.

Sam Densley was the works foreman and kilnman at Combe Hay and lived at Hill View in Odd Down. He was born in 1878 and by 1940 he was only doing light duties.

Ernie Evans was a blender during the 1930s. He died in 1988.

Barry Every was a process worker.

David Every was a process worker.

Roger Every was a process worker.

A. Gerrish ('Smacker') normally drove steam waggon No. 5. Among his other jobs, he used the steam lorry to get coal from the local mines when it was not being delivered by Hamlen's. He got his name from his ability as a boxer. He lived at Rockhall Cottages in Combe Down and was 35 in 1918. In 1921 he had his pay reduced from £4.10.0 because that was £1 more than the drivers in Surrey! He was the brother of Arthur. Dorothy West said of him *'He was a caution, full of jokes and fun and swear words!'*.

Arthur R. Gerrish was called up in the First World War. He was the brother of 'Smacker' Gerrish and lived for a while in Tucking Mill Cottage. He worked at the Pan and at Tucking Mill. He was aged 32 in April 1930, when the plate over the culvert, 6 feet below, cracked with its load of several tons of fuller's earth. It was 6pm and Gerrish was on duty as the night stoker when the accident occurred. It took half an hour to get Gerrish out and oxygen was administered as his lungs had become choked with grit and sand. He was rushed to the Royal United Hospital in Bath, where he recovered. At the time, he had been with the company eight to nine years and lived at Tucking Mill Cottage. He left the company in 1935.

Fred Gerrish worked in the industry in 1895 and was still working at Tucking Mill during the First World War; his son was the stoker, Arthur.

Gifford was in charge of the slurrying plant *i.e.* the Pan in 1925.

Griffin worked with Frank Boddy.

W. (Bill) Gunstone came from the Company's laboratories at Redhill in June 1942, to work at Combe Hay testing the earths being produced.

Gilbert Holley, son of Raymond, was taken on at the age of 14 in October 1946. He did a number of jobs in the industry, finishing as a lorry driver.

Raymond Holley, the brother of Dick Holley, had been a miner in 1922 but was offered lighter work as a bag cleaner in 1925, due to a leg injury sustained while hay making for the Union. In 1935, he deputised for Willis in the engine house when he was ill. For a time he worked at Redhill on the dragline, until he returned as foreman after Ted Densley about 1939. By 1946, he was the supervisor of the millmen. He died in 1955.

W. Dick Holley took on the work as outside fitter in October 1946, maintaining the trams and stoking the Garrett boiler when it was required for the steam winch.

Ian Ingram lived in No. 1 The Firs Cottage and was an electrician.

Jimmy James worked on the coke furnace.

Ron James was an underground maintenance worker.

James Kimber, employed in November 1948 as a second tester in the lab., so the louvre dryer could be run from 7am to 10pm, with shifts on Saturday.

ABOVE: James Palmer and his family c.1916. Alec Palmer is seated between his mother Annie and father. Behind is Albert Palmer, on leave from the Royal Navy with his three sisters Pearl, Ruby and Mary.
BELOW: James Palmer as a young man, c.1892.
ALEC PALMER

Charles E .Lambern was described as a 'fuller's earth getter' (*i.e.* a miner) in October 1916 and exempted from military service.

George Legg was a miner in 1952.

Ernie Love joined in 1941 and worked as a carter and a miner, until his lameness confined him to winding and bag folding.

Gilbert Love went to Redhill as a lorry driver.

Charlie (Jimmy) Love, brother of Ernie, was made foreman miner in April 1942. Later he went to the works at Redhill.

F.W. (Gilbert) Love joined the Company in April 1942 working at Combe Hay. Later, he went to the works at Redhill where he drove a lorry.

Stan Love joined the company on being de-mobbed in December 1945. At first he worked underground and later on in the mill with George Upshall.

W.M. Lovett was 50 in 1918, when he was listed as living at Philip Street in Bath, and was a bag checker and timekeeper.

F. Marsh, the son of R. Marsh, started work in the industry in 1936-37.

R. Marsh was an underground carter who had to retire on health grounds in 1941.

Ted Maule was an electrician.

Samuel Menear was the foreman in 1888 at Wellow for a number of years.

H. (Bert) Miles was in charge of the ponies before mechanisation. He worked on the mills until he retired circa 1959.

C. Fred Morris was married to Maude Staddon in 1900 and his family moved from Packhorse Cottage into Tucking Mill Cottage in September 1914. In 1918, he was allowed by the Recruiting Officer to become an engine driver of the steam waggon instead of a miner; he had been the leading miner at the Top Works. By the spring of 1921, he had left the company, although be appears to have continued to live in the cottage until 1926 or possibly later. He was aged 40 in 1918. His sister Annie was James Palmer's wife. Like the Palmers, Morris may have originated in Wellow.

Albert James Palmer was born in Wellow c1868 and married Annie Morris there. He worked for H.N. Garrett as foreman at Wellow, after Samuel Menear, from at least 1893, for a time also tending the kiln fires at night. From the mid 1890s, he was foreman at Tucking Mill until a disagreement in 1919 with the manager, Owen Keevil. He was given notice to leave in August 1919 and moved to Bradford on Avon. He lived at Tucking Mill House from around 1896 until 1919. He was 50 in 1918, when he supervised the erection of the millhouse and kiln at the Top Works. Both the Palmer and Morris families used to attend the little chapel in Midford. James Palmer died in December 1955 at the age of eighty-eight.

Frank Palmer was the brother of James and was also employed by Garrett at Wellow in April 1893. According to the Wellow time book, he seems to have been the night stoker there after his brother.

Herbert Patch was a stoker and maintenance worker during the First World War at Tucking Mill.

Les Pearce worked in the industry for 27 years in a number of jobs. He was in charge of the coke furnace in the 1960s. He also worked at the Duchy with Bert Upshall.

Brian Rabbits was a miner at the Grove in 1968.

Dennis Rabbits was a miner and lorry driver.

Michael Rabbits was a mill operator.

Bill Shakespeare worked permanently on crushing during the night shift.

Nick Sheppard worked in the mill at Tucking Mill. It is possible that he was related to Walter A. Sheppard.

W. Shellard was offered work in January 1919. He had obviously worked underground before, because O.F. Keevil explained that ponies were now used and that the pit was dry, cool and had good ventilation!

A. Small was employed as an electrician from around 1948 until 1952 to deal with any problems with the new equipment which had been installed after the steam driven plant was replaced. He also helped the fitter with other work.

Dave Smart was a fitter.

Keith Smart was a fitter.

R. Smith lived at Devon Cottages, Odd Down; he was a miner aged 37 in 1918.

Harry Southard retired in 1962.

E.G. Staddon joined the workers at Combe Hay from the Horstmann Gear company in July 1945.

Ern Staddon, who was born in July 1877, moved with his family from Southstoke to No. 1 The Firs at Odd Down around 1925-26 when it was newly built. He began by cleaning the sacks returned by customers before they were used again for another consignment. He then became a miner, before being promoted to underground foreman, a post he held for many years at Combe Hay. Every morning he had to check the safety of the workings. O.F. Keevil called him the most indispensable man at the works. It was his ambition to complete 50 years in the industry but heart trouble forced him to retire early in 1949 just a few months short! He died in 1951.

George Staddon, son of Tom, died in October 1946 when in his fifties. He had been the outside fitter. He served in the First World War and had been a steam waggon driver before enlistment.

James Staddon lived at Underdown, Wellow and joined the workforce in February 1893; he was 45 in 1918. He worked as an engine driver after being sent for training to Redhill in 1918 and also as a banksman. He appears in the photograph of the miners with the tram and of the boiler being delivered to the Top Works in Horsecombe Vale. He usually worked at the Pan. He is also in the photograph of the Yorkshire steam waggon.

Tom Staddon, brother of Ern Staddon, had worked for H.N. Garrett since 1889 and by 1918 it was suggested that he had a lighter job than driving the Yorkshire steam waggon. He lived at The Hermitage in Kilkenny Lane and was 54 in 1918.

Thennier was the fireman in 1885, probably at Wellow and possibly later at Tucking Mill.

George Upshall rejoined the Company from the ARP in 1939 but he had previously worked in the industry in Keevil's day. He had worked at the Duchy site. He retired in 1962.

Albert (Bert) Upshall, the son of G. Upshall, joined the Company as a labourer at the age of 17 in 1942. He finished as factory foreman before going to Redhill on closure in 1980.

John Venables was a welder.

Ern West usually worked at the Top Works until he became the foreman at Tucking Mill in 1925 having previously worked under Wicks. Together in the early 1920s they seem to have run the Tucking Mill operation. Dorothy West, his daughter-in-law remembered that '*every Friday he walked up the Incline* [in Horsecombe Vale] *and along the lane to Southstoke and on to the Upper Combe Hay Works to collect the men's wages*'. West was to continue at Tucking Mill for many years until ill health forced him to retire. In 1933, he was doing all the tank work on his own. When he was ill in 1936, Withers was brought out of retirement to take over. By 1938, he could no longer walk up the hill to the Combe Hay Works and it was decided to keep him on at Tucking Mill as a caretaker for as long as the works existed there. During the Second World War, he was asked to light the kiln when the plant was again required. He died in 1953 aged seventy.

William Wicks worked at Tucking Mill from 1909 and succeeded Palmer there in 1919, when he moved from a cottage owned by the Parfitt estate into Tucking Mill House, until dismissed in 1924. In 1918, he was listed as a kilnman and was then aged 40.

Charlie Willis lived at No. 2 The Firs. He was in charge of the steam winding winch at Combe Hay and was the general mechanic. When he was ill in January 1935, his place was taken, at least for a while, by Ray Holley and Gerrish was brought up from Tucking Mill to assist with the stoking. He died in 1945.

Roy Willshire was the analytical chemist in the last years and then went to Redhill when the works closed.

Ern Withers sometimes worked as a miner at the Top Works and also at Tucking Mill. He lived at Midford and may also have been a carpenter.

Frank Withers was discharged from the army in 1919 and he refused to work on the Garrett engine because he wanted his old job back, driving the Yorkshire steam waggon.

Fred Withers lived at Southstoke; he was a miner aged 45 in 1918. He joined the Union straight from school and did jobs 'up top and underground'. He retired at the age of 72 in 1952. The Withers and Staddons were related.

William Withers had worked at Tucking Mill and on the kilns but was employed on bag folding and cleaning in 1946, being in his mid-sixties by this time. He was blind in one eye and lived in Entry Hill.

Jim Woolman worked in the industry both underground and in the mill room in the mid-1950s for around $2^1/_2$ years.

Others about whom little is known: **Bush, Golledge, Macey, Payton, Rowley, S. Stacey**

STAFFING DURING THE SECOND WORLD WAR

DECEMBER 1939: As trade was fluctuating there were now 3 miners. **R. Marsh** (a carter), 2 kiln men, 2 mill men, 2 on the mixing machine.

APRIL 1941: The longest serving members were **Cole, Holley, Love, Staddon, West** and **Withers**. **Miles** joined the company

MARCH 1942: Four Cornishmen were taken on as miners, one of whom was **W. Hawkey**. Five more Cornishmen joined in December. By now all the men were working a 48 hour week.

By **DECEMBER 1945** the Staff List recorded the following:

Miners: **Busson, E .Love, Golledge**
Carter: **Miles**
Dryers: **Rowley, Bush, Payton, Macey**
Millmen: **R. Holley, G. Upshall, A. Upshall, S. Stacey**
Bag Cleaner: **W. Withers**
(A year later there were more staff on the roll)

NOVEMBER 1946:
6 miners together with **E. Staddon** the underground foreman
2 carters
3 engine house workers
5 louvre dryer workers
4 millmen
W. Withers on bag folding and cleaning

Appendix 2
PRODUCT CODES
Codes used in the fuller's earth industry at Bath

In the early days, the products from Tucking Mill were referred to as 'Washed and Refined' and 'Lump', and from Combe Hay, as finest toilet powder, black clay, blue powder, drab powder and Somerset fine.

Blue Lump	Earth straight from the mine, dried and ready to send to customers like Salomon's in the USA.
Yellow Lump	Earth straight from the mine, dried and ready to send to customers.
AT	'All Top'; it was supplied to Bengers Ltd. Other companies used it in their factories for oil absorption and Derris dust.
AT12	Details unknown.
AT20	'All Top' with some rubbish and used for Derris powder.
B20	Details unknown.
FP	A mixture of 'All Top' and 'All Best' in the ratio 2:1.
FP4	A mixture of 'Best' and 'All Best'.
Fulbent 110	A shovelful of soda ash was added to each barrow load. It was used in asbestos by Cape Asbestos.
Fulbent 120	Less dry and with less soda ash.
Fulbent 150	Used by the Rowney Co. and for oil drilling. Drier than Fulbent 182 and with little soda ash.
Fulbent 182	Very damp earth with soda ash. Used by Boots the Chemists and Shell in their oilfields.
Fulbond No. 1	No soda ash and slightly damp, used by Brockhouse for castings.
Fulbond No. 2	Some soda ash and damp, used in metal casting.
Fulbond No. 3	Less soda ash, otherwise similar to Fulbond No.2.
Fulbond T	Milled North African earth used in UK steel works.
HMT	Yellow used by paint manufacturers.
MM3	Details unknown.
Miner's Powder	Used in mines to counteract the dangers of coal dust causing explosions.
OK	Drab powder.
OK14	A mixture of blue and yellow for Salomon's in the USA.
SB	A mixture of blue and yellow which was less fine than YB20. Used for rubber filling, it also contained China clay.
Special SB	A mixture of Yellow, Blue and China clay.
SH10Y	A blend of SH33 & SH50 and used by National Oil Refineries in South Wales in the mid 1930s.
SH7	Used by ICI at Widnes in Cheshire.
SH10	Contained 10% of German activated earth. Used by oil companies such as National Oil.
SH25	Contained 25% of German activated earth.
SH33	Contained Union Z and was used by the Anglo-Persian Oil Company.
SH50	Contained Union Z and was used by Shell-Mex and BP.
SP4	Dried plain blue earth. It was better than AT and contained no soda ash.
No. 3	A new blend of coarse ground SP4.
Special	Details unknown
Somerset No. 2	Mined from the extreme top of the seam and used for metal moulding.
Union F	German earth.
Union J	German earth.
Union H	German activated earth.
Union Z	German activated earth.
Union 122	A mixture of SP4, Union Z and 249 supplied by Redhill. It was used by Anglo-Persian and National Refineries Ltd
Union Bentonite	Special SP4 and soda ash. Renamed Fulbent.
Union Bentonite No. 1	SP4 and soda ash used in bituminous paints and also in oil drilling. Later renamed Fulbent
UB	Was renamed Fulbent.
YB9	Used by paint manufacturers.
YB20	Careful blend of yellow & blue, milled & screened to 200 mesh, produced 1890-1960, used by Boots and Timothy Whites, chemists
YYB20	Used by Boots the Chemists.

Appendix 3
MACHINE LIST
List of Plant and Machinery used in the Fuller's Earth Industry at Bath

(The information contained in this list has been taken from incomplete records and may not be accurate in every respect)

SITE: COMBE HAY WORKS

MACHINERY	MAKER	DATES	COMMENTS
Steam engine	John Fowler, Leeds	1894-1919	
Griffin engine	Griffin Engineering Co. Ltd Bath	1894-1915	Then transferred probably to Top Works
Engine & boiler	Richard Garrett & Sons, Leiston,	1919-1948	For mill & blender. Garrett CCSV II Suffolk Boiler No. 33537. Superheated 180hp for winding winch. Replaced with electric motor. Metal chimney 60ft high
Annular windmill	Halladay, Illinois, USA	1891-1904	50-60ft diameter
Niagara crusher	W.H. Coward, Bath		May have been installed in the early years
Oil engine 3.25hp (paraffin)	Crossley Bros Ltd, Manchester	1917	For electric lighting
Yorkshire steam waggon	Yorkshire Commercial Motor Co.	1916-27	Sold
Newago separator, plansitter & elevator	Sturtevant Engineering Co. Ltd, Aylesbury	1921	Originally supplied to H.N. Garrett Ltd in 1913-14. Used until 1943
Four kilns			Two steam, two coke
New mill		1913	Steam driven, electrified in 1949
Carey boiler			For the steam pipes under No. 1 kiln
Holman compressed air engine 5-6hp	F.A. Greene & Co. Ltd	1929	Installed underground to drive ventilation fan
Petter 36 hp 2 cylinder engine	R.A. Lister, Dursley	1929-49	Installed in the engine house to drive the above air compressor and pneumatic picks
Elevator mixer	W.F. & O.F. Keevil	1932	Patented by them
Petter engine	R.A. Lister, Dursley		Lighting set
Dust extraction plant	Keith Blackman	1940	
Furnace		1943	Coke fired, later oil-fired, for the rotary dryer electric fans
Coking hoist			Electrified in 1947
Rotary louvre dryer	Dunford & Elliott Ltd, Sheffield	1944	Replaced kilns
Cyclone dust collectors			
BEV electric locomotive	Wingrove & Rogers Ltd	1948	Replaced ponies
Vertical boiler			Power for No. 1 mill. Electrified in 1949
Rotary dressing machine	R.A. Lister, Dursley		
Petter engines, various hp		1940	Several, diesel and petrol. Petrol, later diesel, used on the Duchy incline. For dust plant, for grinder
Diamond single roll crusher	British Jeffrey	1962	

Machinery	Maker	Dates	Comments
Mixing machines	Ransome & Rapier Ltd, Ipswich, Sturtevant Engineering Co. Ltd, Aylesbury	1943	Known as blenders for mixing fuller's earth and soda ash and other additives.
Lightning crusher	Patent Lightning Crusher Co.		Up to 9 tons of fuller's earth per hour
Dust extraction plant			
Soda hopper & measuring machine	Paterson Engineering Co.	1943	
2B 'Dragon' pulveriser or mill	Wm.Johnson & Sons	1943	Electrically powered
Donkey engine vertical boiler			Used for winch when the Garrett boiler was being serviced
No. 2 mill		1943	Electrically powered
Petter diesel engine			
Automatic lighting set		1939-42	Also drove the blender
Steam winch			Hauled trams up the incline
Electric winch	M.B. Wild & Co.	1948	Replaced steam winch

SITE: TUCKING MILL AND HORSECOMBE VALE

Machinery	Maker	Dates	Comments
Cornish multitubular boiler	Possibly by Richard Garrett	1915	Made in 1884, secondhand, fitted with an air bottle
Vertical Boiler		c.1915	The Pan Works
New mill		1916	To grind fuller's earth
Donkey pump,	Birmingham	1918	To supply water to the boilers
Tangye pump			Last used around 1940
Fire kilns			Last used around 1943
Newago separator, plansifter & elevator	Sturtevant Engineering Co. Ltd	1913-14	Moved in 1921 to Combe Hay Works
Boiler	Davey Paxman	1915	Top Works
Griffin engine	Griffin Engineering Co. Ltd, Bath	1915	Top Works, steam from Davey Paxman boiler
Cornish vertical boiler	Stanley Engineering Co.	1915	Top Works
Winding machinery			To work trams on the incline
Tangye engine 3.5-4hp	Birmingham		The Pan Works?
Hot bulb engine, 16 hp kerosine	Tangye, Birmingham?		The Pan Works
Petter oil engine, kerosene	R.A. Lister, Dursley	1920	The Pan Works
Mortar mill	Tiger mill?		The Pan Works
Water wheel			To pump water from the brook into the pan

Acknowledgments

Many people and organisations have assisted me over the years of research into the history of fuller's earth in the Bath area. I am very grateful for all the help and time which they have given me, as without them this story could not have been told. Every effort has been made to trace the sources of extracts and illustrations used throughout this book. I apologise for any errors or omissions.

Peter Addison, Ray Ashman, Chris Barrett, John Beaven-Jones, Andrew Bissex, Hazel Blackmore, M.J. Breakspear, John Brooke, Dr John Broome, Tony Brown, Stuart Burroughs, Gill Carter, Mike Chapman, John Church, Brian Clarke, Jack & Roger Clifford, Lynn Coles, Jasper Cox, Eddie, Roger & Ian Croker, Betty Cross, Joan Day, Geoffrey Evans, Sam Farr, Susan Fox, Dr John G. Fuller, Peter Goodwyn, Keith Green, Jeremy Greenwood, Rosemary Gunstone, Phil Hale, Roger Halse, Walter & Bill Hamlen, Alex & Jeremy Hann, Nellie Hawkins, Gordon Hewlett, Gordon & Patrick Higgs, Jeremy Hignett, Gilbert Holley, Mrs Edna Holmes, Derrick Hunt, Dr W.D. Jones, Alan & Marion Keeling, C. May, Ron Minns, David J. Mitchell, Vera Morris, Mark Neathey, F.J. Norris, Alec Palmer, Florrie Parham, Felicity Pearson, Julian Peters, Noel Pizey, David Pollard, Neville Redvers-Higgins, Jane Richardson, Tom Ridley, Stephen Robbins, Eugene Roberts, Barbara Robertson, Robert H.S. Robertson, Ken Rogers, Brian Roper, John Short, R.M. Skinner, Alison Smith, Diana Smith, Dr Edward Smith, J. Lindsay Smith, R.B.J. Smith, Luke Spanton, Dr Peter Spence, Mary Stacey, Ivor Stephens, Brenda & Charles Swatton, Henry Tanner, Dr Frank Thorn, Prof. Hugh S. Torrens, Edward Turner, Bert Upshall, Owen Ward, Dorothy West, Gwen & Stan Wicks, Dr Lynn Willies, Mr & Mrs C.P. Winpenny, J. Woolman, Anne Wyatt, Michael Yates, Margaret Young.

The Staff at Avon Industrial Buildings Trust; the Staff at Bath Central Library; Colin Johnston and Mary Blagdon at Bath Record Office; the Staff at the Bath Royal Scientific & Literary Institution; Dr Brian Taylor at the British Geological Survey; Judy Copp and Sue Pettit at the University Library (Geology), University of Bristol; Jeremy Pilling at gcp Chartered Architects; Lisa White at the Holburne Museum of Art, Bath; Eugenie Roberts at Laporte Industries Ltd; Alison Bosson at the Library, Monkton Combe School; The Staff at the Somerset County Library and the Somerset Local History Department; The Staff at the Surrey History Centre, Woking; The Director and Staff at the Museum of Bath at Work.

RESOURCES

The Museum of Bath at Work – Fuller's Earth Archives
The Surrey History Centre – Fuller's Earth Records Ref:2876 (Combe Hay and Midford Works).
Bath Record Office – South Stoke Archives
Bath Royal Literary & Scientific Institution – Maps; Combe Hay and Midford
University of Dundee – Roberston R.H.S., Papers and Correspondence

Mention in this book of any transport route, structure or artefact does not imply right of access.

'Woman driving horse laden with fuller's earth'
(from W.H.Pyne's *Rustic Vignettes for Artists and Craftsmen*, 1824 edn.)

Index

PLACES